Dimensions Math®
Workbook 4A

Authors and Reviewers

Jenny Kempe

Bill Jackson

Tricia Salerno

Allison Coates

Cassandra Turner

Singapore Math Inc.

Published by Singapore Math Inc.

19535 SW 129th Avenue
Tualatin, OR 97062
www.singaporemath.com

Dimensions Math® Workbook 4A
ISBN 978-1-947226-24-1

First published 2019
Reprinted 2020 (three times), 2021 (twice), 2022

Printed in China

Acknowledgments

Editing by the Singapore Math Inc. team.
Design and illustration by Cameron Wray with Carli Bartlett.

Contents

Chapter	Exercise	Page

Chapter	Exercise	Page

Chapter	Exercise	Page

This workbook includes **Basics**, **Practice**, **Challenge**, and **Check** sections to review and deepen math skills.

Chapter 1 Numbers to One Million

Basics

 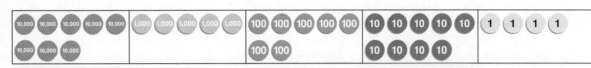

Ten Thousands	Thousands	Hundreds	Tens	Ones
8	5	7	9	4

(a) Complete the place-value chart.

(b) Write the number in numerals. 85,794

(c) The value of the digit in the ten thousands place is _____.

(d) The digit 5 in this number stands for 5 _thousand_ .

(e) Write the number in expanded form. _80000 + 5000 + 700 + 90 × 4_

Practice

2 Write the value of each bolded digit.

(a) **6 4,5 6 4**

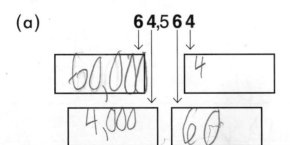

60,000   4

4,000   60

(b) **2 3,0 2 8**

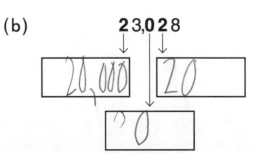

20,000   20

20

(c) In 64,564, the digit 5 stands for 5 _500_ .

(d) In 23,028, the digit _3_ is in the thousands place.

3 (a) $\boxed{87143}$ = 80,000 + 7,000 + 100 + 40 + 3

(b) 60,437 = 60,000 + $\boxed{400}$ + 30 + 7

(c) 14,092 = 10,000 + $\boxed{4000}$ + 92

(d) $\boxed{41,404}$ = 400 + 1,000 + 40,000 + 4

(e) 90,620 = 600 + $\boxed{90,000}$ + 20

(f) 30,030 = $\boxed{30}$ + 30,000

(g) 62,500 = $\boxed{500}$ + 2,000 + 60,000

4 Write the number in numerals.

forty-seven thousand, six hundred ninety-eight	47,698
twenty-three thousand, two hundred four	23,204
thirty-three thousand, thirty-one	33,301
eighteen thousand, forty	18,040
eighty thousand, nine	80,09

5 Write the number in words.

20,640	twenty thousand six hundred
98,700	ninety thousan seven hundre
55,008	fibty five thousand eight
90,077	ninety thousand seventy seven
12,120	twelve thousand one hundre

6 (a) $60{,}000 = \boxed{6}$ ten thousands

(b) $60{,}000 = \boxed{60}$ thousands

(c) $60{,}000 = \boxed{600}$ hundreds

(d) $60{,}000 = \boxed{6{,}000}$ tens

(e) $35{,}000 = \boxed{350}$ hundreds

(f) $10{,}100 = \boxed{1{,}010}$ tens

7 Write the number in numerals.

723 hundreds	72,300
9 ten thousands + 24 tens	90,240
800 hundreds + 60 hundreds + 50 tens	86,500
640 tens + 20 thousands	26,400
92 ones + 4,800 tens	48,092

Challenge

8 Use the clues to find the mystery 5-digit number.

forty

d

Clue 1 All the digits are different.

Clue 2 The thousands digit is 7 more than the tens digit.

Clue 3 The hundreds digit is the sum of the thousands digit and the ones digit.

Clue 4 The total of the digits when added together is 24.

twenty The number is ___18,654___ .

Basics

Hundred Thousands	Ten Thousands	Thousands	Hundreds	Tens	Ones
6	9	8	3	6	5

(a) Write the number shown in numerals. ☐

(b) The value of the digit in the hundred thousands place is _____.

(c) The digit 3 in this number stands for 3 _____.

(d) Write the number in words.

_____

(e) Write the number in expanded form.

_____

Practice

2 Write the value of each bolded digit.

(a) 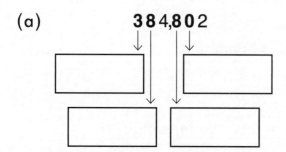 **38**4,**8**02

(b) 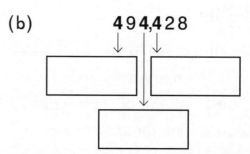 4**94,4**28

(c) In 384,802, the digit 4 stands for 4 _____.

(d) In 494,428, the digit _____ is in the ten thousands place.

3 (a) $\boxed{}$ = 600,000 + 20,000 + 5,000 + 200 + 30 + 9

(b) 160,330 = 100,000 + $\boxed{}$ + 300 + 30

(c) 604,085 = $\boxed{}$ + 4,000 + 80 + 5

(d) $\boxed{}$ = 4,000 + 900,000 + 3 + 10,000 + 50

(e) 110,680 = 600 + $\boxed{}$ + 100,000 + 80

(f) 720,076 = 6 + $\boxed{}$ + 20,000 + 700,000

(g) 500,200 = $\boxed{}$ + 500,000

4 Write the number in numerals.

four hundred thousand, six hundred ninety-eight	
seven hundred twenty-three thousand, one	
eight hundred thousand, forty	
one hundred thirty thousand, thirty-one	
one million	

5 Write the number in words.

271,644	
110,990	
199,009	
100,007	

6 (a) 200,000 = [   ] ten thousands

(b) 200,000 = [   ] hundreds

(c) 120,000 = [   ] tens

(d) 320,000 = [   ] thousands

7 Write the number in numerals.

9,860 hundreds	
80 ten thousands + 60 hundreds + 5 tens	
6,175 tens + 200 thousands	
98 tens + 48 ten thousands	
8 ones + 12,000 tens	
ten hundred thousands	

Challenge

8 Use the clues to find the mystery 6-digit number.

Clue 1 Only two of the digits are the same.
Clue 2 The digit in the tens place is 9 more than the digit in the thousands place.
Clue 3 The number is an odd number.
Clue 4 The digit in the ones place is 5 more than the digit in the hundred thousands place.
Clue 5 The sum of the digits is 34.

The number is _____.

Basics

1 Draw more discs or cross off discs to show the number, and fill in the blanks.

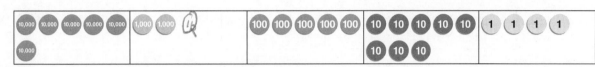

1,000 more than 62,584 is _63,584,000_

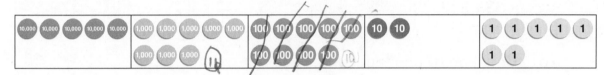

100 more than 58,927 is _58,029_.

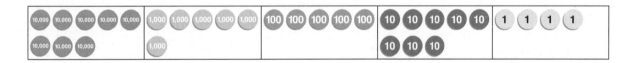

10,000 less than 86,584 is _____.

10 less than 26,009 is _____.

2 (a) 322,523 + 10,000 = [ ]   (b) 141,523 − 10 = [ ]

(c) 14,690 + 100,000 = [ ]   (d) 81,096 − 100 = [ ]

(e) 100,047 − 100 = [ ]   (f) 179,992 + 10 = [ ]

Practice

3 Follow the rules to create the number patterns.

(a) Count on by ten thousand.

97,376				

(b) Count back by one hundred.

333,333				

(c) Count on by one thousand.

208,997				

4 Complete the number patterns.

68,821	68,831				
					78,871
69,039			69,042		
			140,873		118,871
238,876					
		138,874			

5 (a) 689,423 is 1,000 more than _____.

(b) 111,111 is 10,000 more than _____.

(c) _____ is 10,000 less than 50,989.

(d) 400,912 is 10,000 more than _____.

(e) _____ is 1,000 less than 99,999.

(f) _____ is 100 more than 99,999.

(g) _____ is 1 more than 999,999.

6 (a) 24,608 + ☐ = 24,708

(b) 7,012 − ☐ = 6,912

(c) 1,091 − ☐ = 1,081

(d) 8,219 − ☐ = 8,119

(e) 8,930 + ☐ = 9,030

Challenge

7 Complete the number patterns.

(a)

187,174	188,173	189,172			

(b)

51,146	62,136	73,126			

Basics

1 Compare the numbers.

Hundred Thousands	Ten Thousands	Thousands	Hundreds	Tens	Ones
6	3	6	7	9	8
6	3	6	9	2	4

_____ is greater than _____.

Hundred Thousands	Ten Thousands	Thousands	Hundreds	Tens	Ones
4	9	8	3	6	5
4	2	8	9	0	0

_____ is greater than _____.

Hundred Thousands	Ten Thousands	Thousands	Hundreds	Tens	Ones
2	8	0	7	8	2
2	8	0	7	4	6

_____ is less than _____.

Hundred Thousands	Ten Thousands	Thousands	Hundreds	Tens	Ones
	9	8	3	6	5
1	7	3	0	0	8

_____ is less than _____.

Practice

2 Locate the numbers on the number line, then write them in order from least to greatest.

| 45,800 | 56,500 | 65,500 | 36,500 | 56,600 |

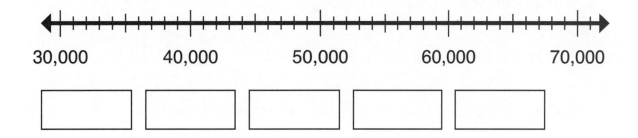

30,000   40,000   50,000   60,000   70,000

| | | | | |

3 Write > or < in each ◯.

(a) 82,262 ◯ 82,623   (b) 918,532 ◯ 981,352

(c) 672,365 ◯ 672,369   (d) 99,856 ◯ 99,865

4 Cross out the numbers that are greater than 55,000 and circle the numbers that are less than 54,600.

| 45,993 | 54,393 | 7,713 | 55,739 | 315,193 |

5 Write the numbers in order from least to greatest.

| 792,793 | 797,913 | 983,713 | 792,739 | 797,193 |

| | | | | |

6 (a) Use the digits 2, 4, 9, 6, 8, and 7 to form the numbers. Use each digit only once for each number.

The greatest 6-digit number. ☐

The least 6-digit number. ☐

The least 6-digit even number. ☐

The greatest 6-digit odd number. ☐

(b) Write the numbers in order from greatest to least.

☐ ☐ ☐ ☐

7 Write > or < in each ◯.

(a) 34,009 + 40 ◯ 8,000 + 4 + 20,000

(b) 90,000 + 60 + 4,200 ◯ 300 + 94,000 + 20

(c) 300 thousands + 70 hundreds ◯ 7,000 tens + 30 ten thousands

8 Read the clues. Then circle the correct number.

Clue 1 The sum of the digits is more than 20.
Clue 2 There are more than 2,000 tens.
Clue 3 There are less than 450 hundreds.

| 38,041 | 26,903 | 15,987 | 40,674 | 135,643 |

Basics

1 Fill in the blanks.

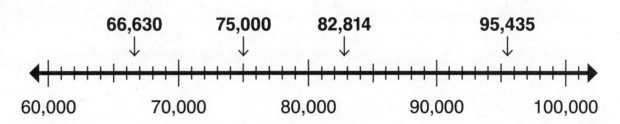

(a) 66,630 is between 60,000 and 70,000. It is nearer to 70,000 than to

60,000. 66,630 is 70,000 when rounded to the nearest _____.

(b) 75,000 is halfway between 70,000 and _____. 75,000 is

_____ when rounded to the nearest ten thousand.

(c) 82,814 is between 80,000 and 90,000. It is nearer to _____

than to _____. 82,814 is _____ when rounded

to the nearest ten thousand.

(d) 95,435 is _____ when rounded to the nearest ten thousand.

(e) When rounding to the nearest ten thousand, if the digit in the

_____ place is _____ or more we round up to the next

ten thousand. When it is _____ or less we round down.

2 Round 48,665 to the nearest thousand.

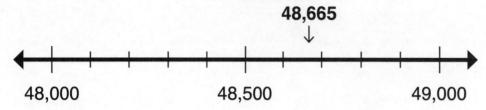

48,665 is _____ when rounded to the nearest thousand.

3 Round 10,025 to the nearest hundred.

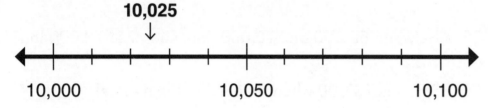

10,025 is _____ when rounded to the nearest hundred.

Practice

4 Indicate the location or approximate location of each number on the number line. Then round each number to the nearest ten thousand.

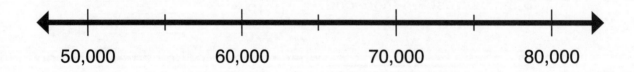

A 65,501 [ ]   **B** 75,000 [ ]

C 51,980 [ ]   **D** 64,999 [ ]

5 Jupiter has a diameter of 88,846 miles at its equator. Round this number to the nearest ten thousand.

[ ]

6 Round each number to the nearest ten thousand.

(a) 10,920 [ ]   (b) 16,501 [ ]

(c) 24,499 [ ]   (d) 97,522 [ ]

7 The table shows the maximum depth of some ocean trenches in feet. Complete the table.

Trench	Depth (ft)	Depth to the nearest		
		10,000 ft	1,000 ft	100 ft
Peru-Chile Trench	26,460			
Kermadec Trench	32,962			
Japan Trench	34,039			
Tonga Trench	35,702			
Mariana Trench	36,070			

8 (a) What is the least whole number that rounds to 230,000 when rounded to the nearest ten thousand?

[ ]

(b) What is the greatest whole number that rounds to 230,000 when rounded to the nearest ten thousand?

[ ]

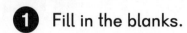
Basics

1 Fill in the blanks.

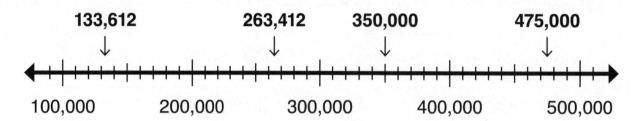

(a) 133,612 is between 100,000 and 200,000. It is nearer to 100,000

than to 200,000. 133,612 is 100,000 when rounded to the nearest

_____.

(b) 263,412 is between 200,000 and 300,000. It is nearer to 300,000

than to 200,000. 263,412 is _____ when rounded to the

nearest hundred thousand.

(c) 350,000 is halfway between _____ and 400,000. 350,000 is

_____ when rounded to the nearest hundred thousand.

(d) 475,000 is _____ when rounded to the nearest hundred thousand.

(e) When rounding to the nearest hundred thousand, if the digit in the

_____ place is _____ or more we round up to the next

hundred thousand. When it is _____ or less we round down.

Practice

2 Indicate the approximate location of 950,749 on each number line with an arrow.

(a)

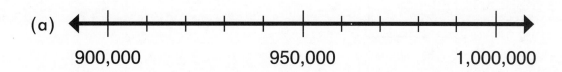

900,000   950,000   1,000,000

950,749 is _____ when rounded to the nearest hundred thousand.

(b)

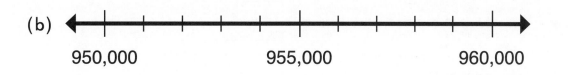

950,000   955,000   960,000

950,749 is _____ when rounded to the nearest ten thousand.

(c)

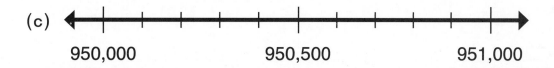

950,000   950,500   951,000

950,749 is _____ when rounded to the nearest thousand.

(d)

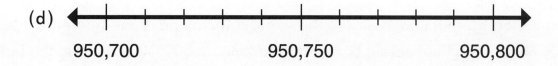

950,700   950,750   950,800

950,749 is _____ when rounded to the nearest hundred.

3 Round each number to the nearest hundred thousand.

(a) 109,920 [   ]

(b) 639,501 [   ]

(c) 250,000 [   ]

(d) 97,522 [   ]

4 The diameter of Jupiter at the equator is 142,984 km. Round this number to:

(a) the nearest hundred thousand. [   ]

(b) the nearest ten thousand. [   ]

(c) the nearest thousand. [   ]

(d) the nearest hundred. [   ]

Challenge

5 A number, when rounded to the nearest thousand, ten thousand, or hundred thousand is 500,000. What is the least whole number it could be?

6 A number, when rounded first to the nearest thousand, then the nearest ten thousand, then the nearest hundred thousand, is 500,000. What is the least whole number it could be?

Basics

1 Add.

(a) 8 thousands + 6 thousands = ☐ thousands

8,000 + 6,000 = ☐

(b) 35 thousands + 9 thousands = ☐ thousands

35,000 + 9,000 = ☐

(c) 14 ten thousands + 23 ten thousands = ☐ ten thousands

140,000 + 230,000 = ☐

2 Subtract.

(a) 8 ten thousands − 6 ten thousands = ☐ ten thousands

80,000 − 60,000 = ☐

(b) 12 thousands − 7 thousands = ☐ thousands

12,000 − 7,000 = ☐

(c) 89 hundreds − 24 hundreds = ☐ hundreds

8,900 − 2,400 = ☐

3 Multiply.

(a) 8 thousands × 6 = ⬚ thousands

8,000 × 6 = ⬚

(b) 4 hundreds × 5 = ⬚ hundreds

400 × 5 = ⬚

(c) 15 ten thousands × 3 = ⬚ ten thousands

150,000 × 3 = ⬚

4 Divide.

(a) 8 hundred thousands ÷ 2 = ⬚ hundred thousands

800,000 ÷ 2 = ⬚

(b) 72 thousands ÷ 6 = ⬚ thousands

72,000 ÷ 6 = ⬚

(c) 40 hundreds ÷ 8 = ⬚ hundreds

4,000 ÷ 8 = ⬚

(d) 15 ten thousands ÷ 5 = ⬚ ten thousands

150,000 ÷ 5 = ⬚

Practice

5 (a) $7,800 + 500 = \boxed{}$

(b) $31,000 - 7,000 = \boxed{}$

(c) $700,000 \times 5 = \boxed{}$

(d) $360,000 \div 6 = \boxed{}$

(e) $5,000 \times 6 = \boxed{}$

(f) $82,000 - 60,000 = \boxed{}$

(g) $100,000 \div 5 = \boxed{}$

(h) $42,000 + 90,000 = \boxed{}$

(i) $120,000 \times 2 = \boxed{}$

(j) $4,000 - 900 = \boxed{}$

(k) $50,000 \div 2 = \boxed{}$

(l) $120,000 + 71,000 = \boxed{}$

(m) $\boxed{} \times 9 = 270,000$

(n) $5,600 \div \boxed{} = 700$

(o) $\boxed{} - 60,000 = 15,000$

(p) $620,000 - \boxed{} = 220,000$

Check

1 (a) In 714,564, the digit 5 stands for 5 _____ .

(b) In the number for four hundred twenty-three thousand, sixty-seven, the value of the digit in the ten thousands place is _____ .

2 (a) Write the numbers in numerals.

90,000 + 5,000 + 50 + 2	
94 ten thousands + 80 hundreds + 70 tens	
9 ten thousands + 7 thousands + 4 hundreds	
The greatest 6-digit even number with 4 in the ten thousands place and all digits different.	
The least 6-digit odd number with 9 in the hundred thousands place and 4 in the thousands place.	

(b) Write the numbers above in order from greatest to least.

3 Continue the number patterns.

(a)

79,325	79,225			

(b)

97,167	98,167			

(c)

248,642	248,742			

4 The diameter of Neptune at the equator is 49,532 km. Round this number to:

(a) the nearest ten thousand.

(b) the nearest thousand.

(c) the nearest hundred.

5 The diameter of Saturn at the equator is 120,536 km. Round this number to:

(a) the nearest hundred thousand.

(b) the nearest ten thousand.

(c) the nearest thousand.

6 Write >, <, or = in each ◯.

(a) 89,000 − 100 ◯ 9,000 × 9

(b) 3,400 + 800 ◯ 5 × 4,000

(c) 48,000 ÷ 8 ◯ 24,000 + 5,000

(d) 230,000 − 80,000 ◯ 62,000 + 37,000 + 8,000 + 13,000

7 A house costs 6 times as much as a car. The car costs $40,000. How much does the house cost?

8 A number is 32,000 less than the quotient of 560,000 ÷ 7. What is the number?

9 A number is rounded to 400,000 when rounded to the nearest ten thousand. What is the least possible and what is the greatest possible whole number it could be?

Challenge

10 There are 5,000 nails in five boxes. The first and second boxes have 2,700 nails altogether. The second and third boxes have 2,000 nails altogether. The third and fourth boxes have 1,800 nails altogether. The fourth and fifth boxes have 1,700 nails altogether. How many nails are in each box?

11 Four blocks, red, blue, green, and yellow, are in a row. The red block is to the right of the blue block, but not directly beside the blue block. The green block is not next to the blue block. The yellow block is next to the red block. What is the order of the blocks from left to right?

Chapter 2 Addition and Subtraction

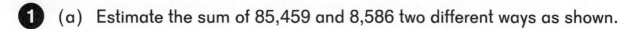

Exercise 1

Basics

1 (a) Estimate the sum of 85,459 and 8,586 two different ways as shown.

$$85{,}459 + 8{,}586$$
$$\downarrow \qquad \downarrow$$
$$90{,}000 + 10{,}000 = \boxed{}$$

$$85{,}459 + 8{,}586$$
$$\downarrow \qquad \downarrow$$
$$85{,}000 + 9{,}000 = \boxed{}$$

(b) Which estimate will be closer to the actual sum?

(c) Which estimate was easier to calculate mentally?

(d) Find the sum of 85,459 and 8,586.

```
    8 5 , 4 5 9
+      8 , 5 8 6
  ┌─┬─┬─┬─┬─┐
  └─┴─┴─┴─┴─┘
```

2 Estimate and then find the sum of 58,965 and 62,432.

$$58{,}965 \quad + \quad 62{,}432$$
$$\downarrow \qquad\qquad \downarrow$$
$$\boxed{} + \boxed{} = \boxed{}$$

Practice

3 (a) Estimate the sum of 462,754 and 63,689 two different ways as shown.

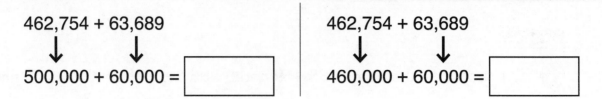

$$462,754 + 63,689$$
$$\downarrow \qquad \downarrow$$
$$500,000 + 60,000 = \boxed{}$$

$$462,754 + 63,689$$
$$\downarrow \qquad \downarrow$$
$$460,000 + 60,000 = \boxed{}$$

(b) Find the sum of 462,754 and 63,689.

```
┌───┬───┬───┬───┬───┬───┐
│ + │   :   :   :   :   │
├───┼───┴───┴───┴───┴───┤
│   │   :   :   :   :   │
└───┴───────────────────┘
```

4 Estimate and then find the sum of 34,842 + 5,783 + 7,874.

$$34,842 \quad + \quad 5,783 \quad + \quad 7,874$$
$$\downarrow \qquad\qquad \downarrow \qquad\qquad \downarrow$$
$$\boxed{} + \boxed{} + \boxed{} = \boxed{}$$

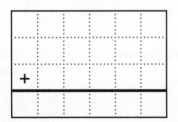

5 How many digits are in the sum of 73,921 and 82,692?

6 Circle the number that is equal to 5,968 + 58,934 + 4,982 without calculating the exact answer.

75,904	14,984	69,884	158,644

7 Estimate and then find the sum.

(a) 25,863 + 97,672 ≈ ☐

25,863 + 97,672 = ☐

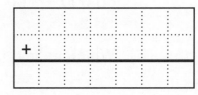

(b) 186,485 + 41,264 + 786 ≈ ☐

186,485 + 41,264 + 786 = ☐

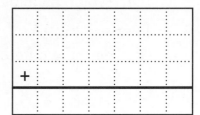

Challenge

8 In the following problem, the letters D, E, and Y stand for different digits. What is the number DYE?

```
    E D D Y
+     Y Y Y
  ---------
    D E E D
```

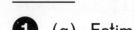

Basics

1 (a) Estimate the difference between 62,342 and 8,724 two different ways as shown.

62,342 – 8,724
↓   ↓
60,000 – 9,000 = [   ]

62,342 – 8,724
↓   ↓
62,000 – 9,000 = [   ]

(b) Which estimate will be closer to the actual difference?

(c) Which estimate was easier to calculate mentally?

(d) Find the difference between 62,342 and 8,724.

```
   6 2 , 3  4  2
 –     8 , 7  2  4
   [  |  |  |  |  ]
```

2 Estimate and then find the difference between 51,582 and 38,958.

51,582 – 38,958
↓   ↓

[   ] – [   ] = [   ]

```
 – [ | | | | ]
   [ | | | | ]
```

Practice

3 (a) Estimate the difference between 852,065 and 57,393 two different ways as shown.

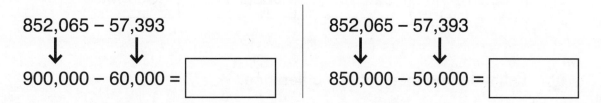

852,065 − 57,393

900,000 − 60,000 = ☐

852,065 − 57,393

850,000 − 50,000 = ☐

(b) Find the difference between 852,065 and 57,393.

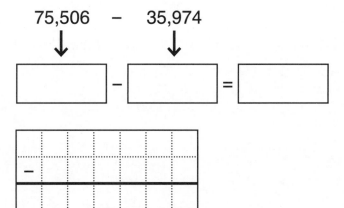

4 Estimate and then find the difference between 35,974 and 75,506.

75,506 − 35,974

☐ − ☐ = ☐

5 Is 624,987 − 78,965 closer to 540,000 or 500,000?

6 How many digits are in the value of 150,747 − 83,965?

7 Circle the number that is equal to 214,094 – 78,934 – 42,762 without calculating the exact answer.

| 80,218 | 92,398 | 92,001 | 106,498 |

8 Estimate and then find the difference.

(a) 80,703 – 72,389 ≈ ⬚

80,703 – 72,389 = ⬚

(b) 416,415 – 41,267 ≈ ⬚

416,415 – 41,267 = ⬚

Challenge

9 In the following problem, the letters A, B, C, D, and E stand for different digits. Find two possible values for ABCDE.

```
   A  B  A  A  B
-        C  B  C
  ──────────────
   D  C  E  D  1
```

Basics

1 (a) 100 = 9 tens + ☐ ones

(b) 1,000 = 9 hundreds + ☐ tens

= 9 hundreds + 9 tens + ☐ ones

(c) 10,000 = 9 thousands + ☐ hundreds

= 9 thousands + ☐ hundreds + 10 tens

= 9 thousands + 9 hundreds + ☐ tens + 10 ones

2 9,000 = 5,000 + ☐   3,000 + ☐ = 9,000

900 = 300 + ☐   600 + ☐ = 900

90 = 70 + ☐   0 + ☐ = 90

10 = 8 + ☐   2 + ☐ = 10

10,000 = 5,378 + ☐   3,602 + ☐ = 10,000

4,000 + ☐ = 9,000   0 + ☐ = 9,000

900 + ☐ = 900   700 + ☐ = 900

10 + ☐ = 100   60 + ☐ = 100

4,910 + ☐ = 10,000   760 + ☐ = 10,000

Practice

3 10,000 − 4,321 = ☐   1,000 − 844 = ☐

60,000 − 4,321 = ☐   72,000 − 844 = ☐
  ╱   ╲   ╱   ╲
50,000 10,000   71,000 1,000

100 − 82 = ☐   100 − 55 = ☐

2,400 − 82 = ☐   89,600 − 55 = ☐
  ╱   ╲   ╱   ╲
2,300 100   89,500 100

70,000 − 7,096 = ☐   23,000 − 191 = ☐
  ╱ ╲   ╱ ╲
☐   10,000   ☐   1,000

4 (a) 4,930 + ☐ = 10,000

(b) ☐ + 721 = 10,000

(c) 42 + ☐ = 10,000

(d) 7,008 + ☐ = 30,000

5 (a) 10,000 − 8,444 = ☐

(b) 40,000 − 6,009 = ☐

(c) 80,000 − 772 = ☐

(d) 20,000 − 66 = ☐

6 (a) $41,000 - 430 =$

(b) $87,500 - 82 =$

(c) $24,000 - \boxed{} = 310$

(d) $92,400 - \boxed{} = 44$

7 A bin had 10,000 nails. 5,346 were used, then another 715 were used. How many nails are left in the bin?

8 A club raised $20,000 in a fundraiser. They spent $13,750 of it so far. How much money do they still have?

Challenge

9 (a) $100,000 - 94,321 =$

(b) $500,000 - 20,570 =$

(c) $789,000 - 6,008 =$

(d) $1,000,000 - 433,860 =$

Basics

1 $5{,}784 + 998 = 5{,}782 + \boxed{} = \boxed{}$

5,782   2

$5{,}784 \xrightarrow{\ -\ 2\ } \boxed{} \xrightarrow{\ +\ 1{,}000\ } \boxed{}$

$5{,}784 \xrightarrow{\ +\ 1{,}000\ } \boxed{} \xrightarrow{\ -\ 2\ } \boxed{}$

2 $5{,}784 - 998 = 4{,}784 + \boxed{} = \boxed{}$

4,784 1,000

$5{,}784 \xrightarrow{\ +\ 2\ } \boxed{} \xrightarrow{\ -\ 1{,}000\ } \boxed{}$

$5{,}784 \xrightarrow{\ -\ 1{,}000\ } \boxed{} \xrightarrow{\ +\ 2\ } \boxed{}$

3

$4{,}327 + 99 = \boxed{}$

4,326   1

$4{,}327 - 99 = \boxed{}$

4,227   100

$4{,}327 + 299 = \boxed{}$

4,326   1

$4{,}327 - 299 = \boxed{}$

4,027   300

$4{,}327 + 1{,}999 = \boxed{}$

4,326   1

$4{,}327 - 1{,}999 = \boxed{}$

2,327 2,000

4 (a) 50 + 60 = ⬚

(b) 450 + 60 = ⬚

(c) 7,450 + 60 = ⬚

(d) 7,458 $\xrightarrow{+60}$ ⬚ $\xrightarrow{-1}$ ⬚

(e) 7,458 + 59 = ⬚ + 60 = ⬚

         ⁄   ＼

     7,457   1

5 (a) 21 − 4 = ⬚

(b) 210 − 40 = ⬚

(c) 3,210 − 40 = ⬚

(d) 3,218 $\xrightarrow{-40}$ ⬚ $\xrightarrow{+2}$ ⬚

(e) 3,218 − 38 = ⬚ + 2 = ⬚

        ⁄   ＼

    3,178   40

6 (a) 4,387 $\xrightarrow{+40}$ ⬚ $\xrightarrow{-1}$ ⬚

     4,387 + 39 = ⬚

(b) 6,228 $\xrightarrow{-40}$ ⬚ $\xrightarrow{+1}$ ⬚

     6,228 − 39 = ⬚

Practice

 Add or subtract.

8,432 + 99 **C**	9,007 − 98 **H**	10,000 − 8,492 **T**
3,889 + 998 **M**	9,868 − 999 **V**	6,129 + 498 **R**
984 + 799 **S**	4,725 + 89 **G**	10,000 − 398 **N**
9,000 − 998 **I**	10,000 − 28 **K**	7,407 + 1,998 **O**
9,921 − 2,999 **E**	987 + 78 **P**	10,000 − 3,702 **A**

Write the letters that match the answers and learn a fun fact.

1,783	8,909	6,298	6,627	9,972	1,783	1,873	8,531	6,298	9,602

9,602	6,922	8,869	6,922	6,627	8,431	1,783	1,508	9,405	1,065

8,969	1,873	4,887	9,405	8,869	8,002	9,602	4,814	8,431	8,969

Challenge

8

5,400 + 800 = ☐   4,200 – 600 = ☐

57 + 7 = ☐   81 – 5 = ☐

5,457 + 807 = ☐   4,281 – 605 = ☐

25,000 + 8,000 = ☐   46,000 – 9,000 = ☐

213 + 8 = ☐   775 – 8 = ☐

25,213 + 8,008 = ☐   46,775 – 9,008 = ☐

9 (a) 3,864 + 606 = ☐

(b) 9,472 – 508 = ☐

(c) 72,509 + 6,005 = ☐

(d) 13,381 – 4,007 = ☐

10 399 + 498 + 597 + 696 = ☐

11 30,022 + 29,998 + 29,980 + 30,010 = ☐

Basics

1 For each problem, finish labeling the bar model with the information given in the problems. Mark the quantity that needs to be found with a question mark. Then solve the problem.

(a) There are 3 laptops for sale at a store. Laptop A costs $1,200 and is $900 less than Laptop B. Laptop C costs $285 more than Laptop B. How much do all three laptops cost altogether?

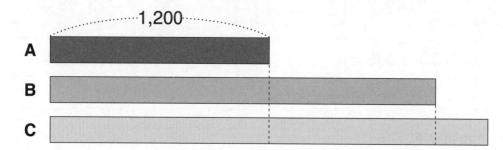

(b) A bookstore sold 435 fewer books on Saturday than on Friday. On Sunday, it sold 3,260 books, which was 1,420 more books than on Friday. How many books did it sell altogether during the three days?

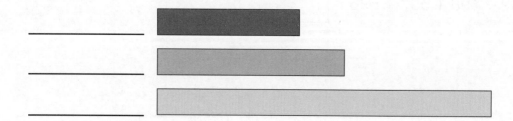

(c) There were 8,435 more kilograms of beans in Bin A than in Bin B in a warehouse. After 2,630 kilograms of beans were taken out of Bin A, 11,550 kilograms of beans were left in Bin A. How many kilograms of beans were in Bin B?

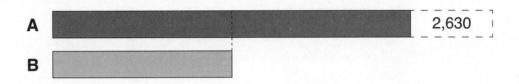

(d) There were 456 fewer students in School A than in School B. After 162 students transferred from School B to School A, how many more students were in School B than School A?

Practice

2 4,693 concert tickets were sold on Tuesday. 1,840 more concert tickets were sold on Monday than on Wednesday. 1,524 fewer concert tickets were sold on Tuesday than on Wednesday. How many concert tickets were sold on Monday?

3 String A is 560 cm shorter than String C and 120 cm longer than String B. String C is 2,320 cm long. How long are Strings A and B together?

4 There were 1,430 trees in an orchard. 750 of them were apple trees and the rest were peach trees. After 82 of the apples trees died, and 35 more peach trees were planted, how many more peach trees than apple trees were there?

5 There were 1,350 cars in Lot A. After 420 cars were moved from Lot B to Lot A, there were 1,720 cars in Lot B. How many cars are in both lots altogether?

Check

1 Estimate and then find the values.

(a) $45{,}846 + 32{,}185 \approx$ ☐

$45{,}846 + 32{,}185 =$ ☐

(b) $345{,}000 - 83{,}723 \approx$ ☐

$345{,}000 - 83{,}723 =$ ☐

(c) $62{,}089 + 490{,}076 \approx$ ☐

$62{,}089 + 490{,}076 =$ ☐

(d) $87{,}002 - 49{,}725 \approx$ ☐

$87{,}002 - 49{,}725 =$ ☐

2 (a) $4{,}892 + 99 =$ ☐   (b) $10{,}000 - 985 =$ ☐

(c) $70{,}000 - 4{,}568 =$ ☐   (d) $892 + 498 =$ ☐

(e) $7{,}718 + 89 =$ ☐   (f) $6{,}500 - 87 =$ ☐

(g) $82{,}780 - 998 =$ ☐   (h) $84{,}345 + 142 =$ ☐

3 There were 5,878 passengers on a ship. At the end of a week-long cruise, 4,341 people got off, and the rest stayed on for the next week. 4,362 more people got on for the next week.

(a) Estimate how many people are now on the ship.

(b) Find how many people are now on the ship.

(c) The capacity of the ship is 6,000 passengers. By how much is the ship under capacity for the second week?

4 On a cruise ship, 479,314 gallons of fresh water were consumed in one day. 13,174 of those gallons were frozen for ice. How many gallons of water were not used for ice?

5 A cruise ship needs to have at least 40,000 pounds of potatoes for a two-week cruise. It has 2,786 pounds left over from the last trip. It can order potatoes from a supplier in amounts rounded to the nearest thousand pounds. How many pounds of potatoes must it order?

6 For a one-week cruise, a cruise ship had 3,450 more pounds of white flour than whole wheat flour and 1,250 pounds less rye flour than whole wheat flour. It had 2,240 pounds of rye flour. How many pounds of the three types of flour did it have altogether?

7 On a cruise, there were 3,935 adults. There were 1,980 fewer children than adults. After 2,560 adults and 1,420 children got off the ship for the day at one stop, how many passengers were left on the ship?

Challenge

8 There are 1,000 flags in a row. From left to right, the 60th to 290th flags are blue. From right to left, the 150th to 410th flags are blue. The rest of the flags are red. How many red flags are there?

9 15 digits are in a row. The sum of every 3 consecutive digits is 10. What are the values of P and Q?

1	P				Q									8

10 In the following problem, the letters X, Y, and Z stand for different digits. What is the greatest possible sum?

```
    X  2  Y  Z
    Z  Y  3  X
    Y  Z  X  4
+   2  X  Y  Z
  ┌──┬──┬──┬──┐
  │  │  │  │  │
  └──┴──┴──┴──┘
```

11 **Step 1** Pick any 4-digit number where the thousands digit and hundreds digit are different.

Example

4,632

Step 2 Reverse its digits.

2,364

Step 3 Find the difference between these two numbers.

4,632 − 2,364 = 2,268

Step 4 Reverse its digits.

8,622

Step 5 Find the sum of the difference and its reverse.

2,268 + 8,622 = 10,890

Do these 5 steps with other numbers. What do you observe?

12 **Step 1** Use any three different digits to make the greatest and least 3-digit number.

Example

743 and 347

Step 2 Find the difference between them.

743 − 347 = 396

Step 3 Continually repeat steps 1 and 2 using the digits from this new number.

963 − 369 = 594

...

What happens?

Try some other numbers. Does the same thing happen?

Chapter 3 Multiples and Factors

Basics

1 (a) Find the first ten multiples of 7.

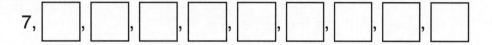

7, ☐, ☐, ☐, ☐, ☐, ☐, ☐, ☐, ☐

(b) What is the 13th multiple of 7?

(c) What is the 7th multiple of 20?

(d) Is 105 a multiple of 7?

2 Without dividing, how can you easily determine if a number is...

(a) a multiple of 2?

(b) a multiple of 3?

(c) a multiple of 5?

3 Is 105 a multiple of 2, 3, or 5?

Practice

4 (a) List the first twelve multiples of 5.

(b) List the first four multiples of 17.

5 Circle the numbers that are multiples of 6.

6	16	34	54	56	88	96

6 Circle the numbers that are multiples of 8.

6	16	34	54	56	88	96

7 (a) What is the 12th multiple of 9?

(b) What is the 11th multiple of 10?

(c) Is 110 a multiple of 4?

(d) Is 136 a multiple of 4?

| 15 | 36 | 60 | 64 | 78 | 120 | 216 |

Which of the above numbers are multiples of:

(a) 2?   (b) 9?

(c) 3?   (d) 6?

(e) 5?   (f) 10?

Challenge

9 A certain number is a multiple of 8. When 4 is added to it, the sum is the 4th multiple of 13. What is the number?

10 In the pattern below, what shape will be in the 32nd position?

Basics

1 List the first twelve multiples of each number. Then list the common multiples.

(a) Multiples of 3:

Multiples of 4:

First three common multiples of 3 and 4:

(b) Multiples of 6:

Multiples of 9:

First three common multiples of 6 and 9:

2 List the first eight multiples of 8.

Which of these are also multiples of 6?

What are the first two common multiples of 6 and 8?

3 21 is a common multiple of _____ and _____.

Is 42 also a common multiple of those two numbers?

Give the next two common multiples of those two numbers.

Practice

4 Find the first two common multiples of 8 and 12.

5 Circle the numbers that are common multiples of 3 and 4.

4	12	28	32	48	72

6 Find the first three common multiples of 2, 3, and 4.

7 Find the first three common multiples of 3, 5, and 6.

8 Three numbers have a common multiple of 24. What is another common multiple of those three numbers?

9 There are between 50 and 100 blocks. The blocks can be stacked equally into either 7 stacks or 5 stacks. How many blocks are there?

10 3 bells ring at intervals of 3, 6, and 8 minutes. If they all rang together at 3:00, what time will they ring together again?

Challenge

11 A number, when divided by 5 gives a remainder of 3, and when divided by 4 gives a remainder of 1. What is the least number it could be?

12 A number, X, is a common multiple of 2, 6, and 8. Another number, Y, is a common multiple of 3, 5, and 10. What is the least possible value for X + Y?

Basics

1 Find the factors of 16.

$16 = \boxed{} \times \boxed{}$

$16 = \boxed{} \times \boxed{}$ $16 = \boxed{} \times \boxed{}$

The factors of 16 are _____, _____, _____, _____, and _____.

2 (a) Find the factors of 35.

$35 = 1 \times \boxed{}$ $35 = 5 \times \boxed{}$ $35 = 7 \times \boxed{}$

The factors of 35 are _____, _____, _____, and _____.

(b) How can we tell without dividing that 2, 4, and 6 are not factors of 35?

3 (a) $8\overline{)9\ \ 4}$

Is 8 a factor of 94?

(b) $8\overline{)9\ \ 6}$

Is 8 a factor of 96?

Practice

4 Write "yes" or "no."

Number	Is 2 a factor?	Is 3 a factor?	Is 5 a factor?
5			
15			
36			
60			
73			
84			
100			
114			
120			

5 (a) Circle the numbers that are factors of 18.

1	2	3	4	5	6	7

(b) Circle the numbers that are factors of 48.

3	5	6	8	10	48	96

(c) Circle the numbers that have 6 as a factor.

1	3	6	26	30	72	100

6 Find all the factors of each of the following numbers. List them in order from least to greatest.

(a) 56

(b) 64

(c) 80

(d) 96

(e) 120

7 32 sandwiches are arranged on plates so each plate gets the same number of sandwiches. What are the possible numbers of plates needed?

8 54 flowers are to be arranged in an even number of vases so that each vase has the same number of flowers. There needs to be at least 5 vases and at most 20 vases. What are the possible numbers of vases needed?

Challenge

9 Circle the numbers that have an odd number of factors.

9	10	15	25	49	81	121

10 What are the four numbers less than 50 that have exactly 3 factors?

Basics

1 (a) Find all the factors of each of the following numbers.

19	20
21	23
27	29

(b) Which of these numbers have only 2 factors, and so are prime numbers?

(c) Which of these numbers have more than 2 factors, and so are composite numbers?

2 What two numbers are neither prime nor composite?

Practice

 3 (a) The prime numbers less than 10 are _____, _____, _____,

and _____.

(b) The only even number that is a prime number is _____.

(c) Other than 5, which is prime, all odd numbers with _____ in the ones place are composite numbers since they are multiples of 5.

(d) Which of the following remaining odd numbers less than 100 are composite numbers? Cross them off.

11	13	17	19	21	23	27	29
31	33	37	39	41	43	47	49
51	53	57	59	61	63	67	69
71	73	77	79	81	83	87	89
91	93	97	99				

(e) Using the above information, list the 25 prime numbers less than 100.

4 Twin primes are pairs of prime numbers that have a difference of 2, for example, 11 and 13. Find all the twin primes less than 100.

5 16 can be expressed as the sum of two prime numbers: 16 = 11 + 5. Find three other numbers greater than 10 and show how they can each be expressed as the sum of two prime numbers.

6 An emirp is a pair of prime numbers with reversed digits, such as 37 and 73. List all the pairs of two-digit emirps.

7 Circle the number in the grid that obeys the following two rules.

Rule 1 The number is not in a row that contains a prime number.
Rule 2 The number is not in a column that contains a number that has an odd number of factors.

82	27	12	31
10	19	42	36
81	40	28	18
79	25	65	34

Basics

 (a) $12 = 1 \times$ ☐

$12 = 2 \times$ ☐

$12 = 3 \times$ ☐

The factors of 12 are _____, _____, _____, _____, _____,

and _____.

(b) $20 = 1 \times$ ☐

$20 = 2 \times$ ☐

$20 = 4 \times$ ☐

The factors of 20 are _____, _____, _____, _____, _____,

and _____.

(c) The common factors of 12 and 20 are _____, _____, and _____.

(d) Which common factor of 12 and 20 is greatest? _____

2 Circle common factors of 36 and 42.

| 2 | 3 | 6 | 9 | 12 | 18 | 36 |

Practice

3 (a) Circle the numbers that have 4 and 5 as common factors.

| 5 | 20 | 35 | 40 | 48 | 65 | 100 |

(b) Circle the numbers that have 2, 3, and 6 as common factors.

| 6 | 18 | 24 | 30 | 42 | 81 | 120 |

4 Find all the common factors of each set of numbers.

(a) 24, 30

(b) 48, 84

(c) 35, 37, 90

5 75 black pens, 45 blue pens, and 30 red pens need to be put in boxes so that each box has the same number of each color of pen. What is the greatest number of boxes needed, and how many of each color pen will be in each box?

Challenge

6 Continue a path through the maze. In order to move from one square to an adjacent square, the two numbers must have a common factor other than 1.

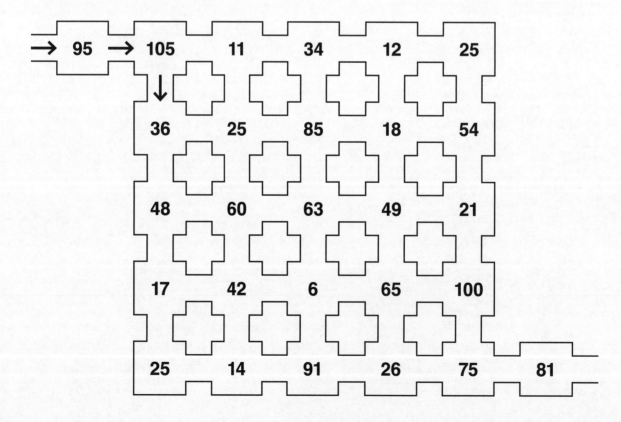

3-5 Common Factors

Check

1 List the multiples of 6 that are between 30 and 80.

2 What number less than 200 is the greatest multiple of 5?

3 Find the sum of the first four multiples of 3 and the first three multiples of 4.

4 Find the first three common multiples of each set of numbers.

(a) 6, 15

(b) 8, 10, 12

5 (a) What number is the least multiple of 38?

(b) What number is the greatest possible factor of 120?

6 A 2-digit even number has 5 and 9 as factors. What number is it?

7 A 2-digit odd number is a factor of 54 and a multiple of 9. What number is it?

8 Find all the common factors of each set of numbers.

(a) 30, 45

(b) 30, 40, 100

9 Can the product of two prime numbers be an even number? Explain why or why not.

10 Can the product of two prime numbers be a prime number? Explain why or why not.

11 A blue light blinks every 10 seconds. A red light blinks every 12 seconds. A green light blinks every 8 seconds. If all three lights just blinked at the same time, in how many seconds will they again blink at the same time?

12 A red ribbon is 64 inches long, a blue ribbon is 80 inches long, and a yellow ribbon is 96 inches long. They are all to be cut into shorter pieces of the same length without any leftover pieces. What is the longest possible length of each ribbon? How many pieces of each color of ribbon will there be?

Challenge

13 A group of people are traveling together to camp. Each car can hold 5 people. If 4 people were to go in each car, there would be 3 people left over. If 5 people were to go in each car, there would be room for 2 more people in the last car. How many people and how many cars are there?

14 Emma found the difference between two prime numbers is 15. What are the two prime numbers?

15 A Sophie Germain prime is a prime number such that if 1 is added to twice that number, the answer is also a prime number. For example, 3 is a Sophie Germain prime number because $2 \times 3 + 1 = 7$, which is also prime. Find all the Sophie Germain primes that are less than 50.

Chapter 4 Multiplication

Basics

1 (a) $12 \times 3 = 30 + 6 =$ ☐

(b) 12 hundreds $\times 3 =$ ☐ hundreds $=$ ☐

(c) 12 thousands $\times 3 =$ ☐ thousands $=$ ☐

2 (a) $35 \times 4 =$ ☐ $+ 20 =$ ☐

(b) $350 \times 4 =$ ☐

(c) $3,500 \times 4 =$ ☐

(d) $35,000 \times 4 =$ ☐

3 (a) $100 \times 7 =$ ☐   (b) $200 \times 7 =$ ☐

  $99 \times 7 =$ ☐ $199 \times 7 =$ ☐

(c) $300 \times 7 =$ ☐   (d) $3,000 \times 7 =$ ☐

  $299 \times 7 =$ ☐ $2,999 \times 7 =$ ☐

Practice

 Use mental calculation to find the products.

(a) 100 × 6 =

(b) 150 × 9 =

(c) 40,000 × 8 =

(d) 1,300 × 5 =

(e) 2,500 × 4 =

(f) 910 × 2 =

(g) 15,000 × 3 =

(h) 7,200 × 8 =

(i) 5 × 42,000 =

(j) 7 × 3,300 =

(k) 98 × 6 =

(l) 5 × 399 =

(m) 3 × 599 =

(n) 6,999 × 4 =

5 A 24-foot-wide frame for a greenhouse costs $4,999. A farm wants to buy 5 of them. What will be the total cost?

6 The pediatric clinic needs 250 bandages a week. The central clinic needs 600 bandages a week. How many bandages should the two clinics order to have enough for 8 weeks?

Basics

1 (a) Complete the following estimates for the product of 5,172 and 4.

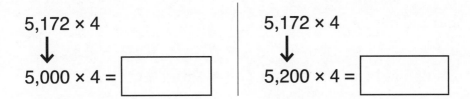

5,172 × 4
↓
5,000 × 4 = ☐

5,172 × 4
↓
5,200 × 4 = ☐

(b) Fill in the missing numbers or digits for each calculation method.

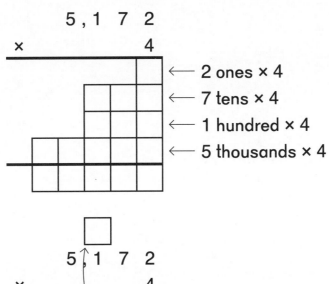

```
    5 , 1  7  2
×            4
─────────────────
              ← 2 ones × 4
              ← 7 tens × 4
              ← 1 hundred × 4
              ← 5 thousands × 4
─────────────────
```

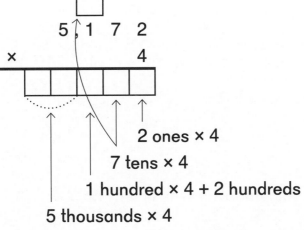

```
    5 , 1  7  2
×            4
─────────────────
```

2 ones × 4
7 tens × 4
1 hundred × 4 + 2 hundreds
5 thousands × 4

(c) Compare the estimates to the actual product.
Which estimate was lower?
Which estimate was higher?
Which estimate was closer?

Practice

2 (a) Dion estimated the product of 3,521 and 3 to be 12,000. With what number did he replace 3,521?

(b) Mei estimated the product of 3,521 and 3 to be 9,900. With what number did she replace 3,521?

(c) Whose estimate will be closer to the actual product?

(d) Find the product of 3,521 and 3.

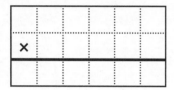

3 Is 9,183 × 3 greater than or less than 25,000?

4 The product of 4,962 and 8 is closest to which multiple of 10,000?

5 Are the following products reasonable? Why or why not?

(a) 7 × 986 = 6,902

(b) 71,081 × 8 = 57,448

6 Estimate and then find the exact product.

(a) $8,292 \times 3 \approx$ ___

$8,292 \times 3 =$ ___

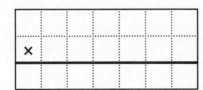

(b) $6,710 \times 8 \approx$ ___

$6,710 \times 8 =$ ___

(c) $6,114 \times 7 \approx$ ___

$6,114 \times 7 =$ ___

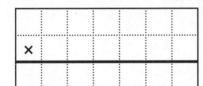

(d) $11,771 \times 6 \approx$ ___

$11,771 \times 6 =$ ___

7 A backhoe costs $12,199. An excavator costs $165,599. A construction company wants to buy 4 backhoes and 1 excavator. What is the total cost?

Challenge

8 Find the products. Do you notice a pattern?

$1,089 \times 1 = $ ⬚

$1,089 \times 2 = $ ⬚

$1,089 \times 3 = $ ⬚

$1,089 \times 4 = $ ⬚

$1,089 \times 5 = $ ⬚

$1,089 \times 6 = $ ⬚

$1,089 \times 7 = $ ⬚

$1,089 \times 8 = $ ⬚

$1,089 \times 9 = $ ⬚

9 In the following problem, the letters S, T, O, and P stand for different digits. What is the number POTS?

$$
\begin{array}{r}
S \; T \; O \; P \\
\times \qquad\quad 4 \\
\hline
P \; O \; T \; S
\end{array}
$$

Basics

1 (a) Complete the following estimations for the product of 2,745 and 8.

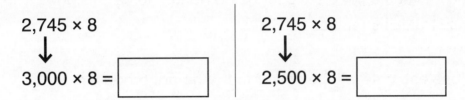

$2{,}745 \times 8$
↓
$3{,}000 \times 8 = $ ☐

$2{,}745 \times 8$
↓
$2{,}500 \times 8 = $ ☐

(b) Fill in the missing numbers or digits for each calculation method.

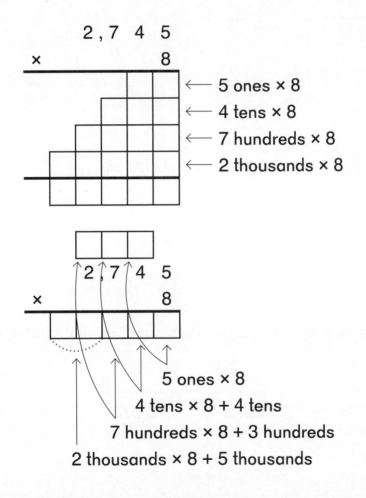

2 , 7 4 5
×   8

←— 5 ones × 8
←— 4 tens × 8
←— 7 hundreds × 8
←— 2 thousands × 8

2 , 7 4 5
×   8

5 ones × 8
4 tens × 8 + 4 tens
7 hundreds × 8 + 3 hundreds
2 thousands × 8 + 5 thousands

(c) Compare the estimates to the actual product.

Which estimate was lower?

Which estimate was higher?

Which estimate was closer?

Practice

2 (a) Alex estimated the product of 52,891 and 4 to be 200,000. With what number did he replace 52,891?

(b) Sofia estimated the product of 52,891 and 4 to be 212,000. With what number did she replace 52,891?

(c) Whose estimate will be closer to the actual product?

(d) Find the product of 52,891 and 4.

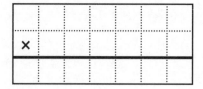

3 Is the product of 84,984 and 5 closer to 400,000 or 500,000?

4 Circle the number that is equal to 8,563 × 6 without calculating the exact product.

| 524,318 | 51,378 | 51,372 | 5,372 |

5 Which of the following gives the greatest product?

| 6,953 × 6 | 5,235 × 8 | 5,673 × 9 |

6 Estimate and then find the exact product.

(a) $7{,}884 \times 4 \approx$ [ ]

$7{,}884 \times 4 =$ [ ]

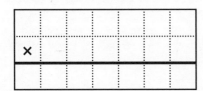

(b) $3{,}482 \times 5 \approx$ [ ]

$3{,}482 \times 5 =$ [ ]

(c) $6{,}908 \times 7 \approx$ [ ]

$6{,}908 \times 7 =$ [ ]

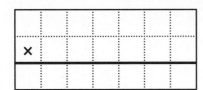

(d) $27{,}448 \times 6 \approx$ [ ]

$27{,}448 \times 6 =$ [ ]

7 A leap year occurs every 4 years. A standard year has 365 days and a leap year has 366 days. How many days are in 4 consecutive years?

Challenge

8 Find the products. Do you notice a pattern?

9,999 × 1 = [   ]

9,999 × 2 = [   ]

9,999 × 3 = [   ]

9,999 × 4 = [   ]

9,999 × 5 = [   ]

9,999 × 6 = [   ]

9,999 × 7 = [   ]

9,999 × 8 = [   ]

9,999 × 9 = [   ]

9,999 × 10 = [   ]

9 In the following problem, the letters G, R, E, A, and T stand for different digits. What is the number GREAT?

```
    1 G R E A T
  ×           3
  ─────────────
    G R E A T 1
```

Check

1 Is the product of 87,984 and 6 closer to 500,000 or 600,000?

2 Estimate to arrange the expressions in order from least to greatest.

16,953 × 3	21,992 × 2	7,673 × 7	4,813 × 9
A	B	C	D

3 Estimate and then find the exact product.

(a) 3,806 × 7 ≈ ☐

3,806 × 7 = ☐

(b) 9,458 × 8 ≈ ☐

9,458 × 8 = ☐

(c) 73,987 × 2 ≈ ☐

73,987 × 2 = ☐

4 There are 5,280 feet in 1 mile. How many feet are in 8 miles?

5 An artist sold 5 paintings for $3,410 each. If the frame, canvas, paint, and other material for each painting cost $155, how much profit did he make from the paintings after subtracting the cost of materials?

6 An aquarium had 3,876 visitors one day. Each visitor was given 2 drink coupons and 3 food coupons to use at the food court. How many coupons were given out?

7 To raise money to rescue marine animals, 3 corporations pledged to give $55,600 each to the charity if their total contributions were matched by other donors. The amount was matched and an additional $4,590 was raised. How much money was raised for the charity in all?

Challenge

8 Find the missing digits.

(a)

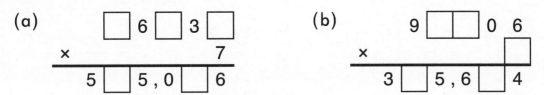

```
    ☐ 6 ☐ 3 ☐
  ×           7
  ─────────────
  5 ☐ 5 , 0 ☐ 6
```

(b)

```
      9 ☐   0 6
  ×           ☐
  ─────────────
  3 ☐ 5 , 6 ☐ 4
```

9 Alex's estimate: 6 × 896 ≈ 10 × 896 = 8,960

Emma's estimate: 6 × 896 ≈ 6 × 900 = 5,400

Both of them increased one factor by 4, but one of the estimates is much closer to the actual answer. Without calculating the answer, determine which estimate is closer and why.

10 In a large tank at an aquarium, there were twice as many jellyfish as water snails. After 430 snails were removed from the tank, there were 3 times as many jellyfish as water snails. How many jellyfish were there?

Basics

1 (a) 90 × 10 = [　　　]

(b) 900 × 10 = [　　　]

(c) 46 × 10 = [　　　]

(d) 46 × 100 = [　　　]

(e) 80 × 10 = [　　　]

(f) 800 × 100 = [　　　]

2 (a) 6 × 3 = [　　　]

(b) 60 × 30 = [　　　]

(c) 600 × 3 = [　　　]

(d) 6 × 300 = [　　　]

(e) 600 × 30 = [　　　]

(f) 60 × 300 = [　　　]

3 (a) 62 × 30 = 62 × 3 × 10

(b) 620 × 30 = 620 × 3 × 10

= [　　　] × 10

= [　　　] × 10

= [　　　]

= [　　　]

4 Write the missing digits.

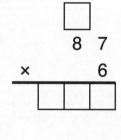

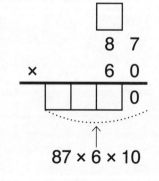

87 × 6 × 10

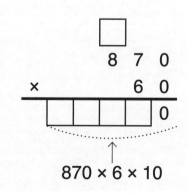

870 × 6 × 10

Practice

5 Multiply.

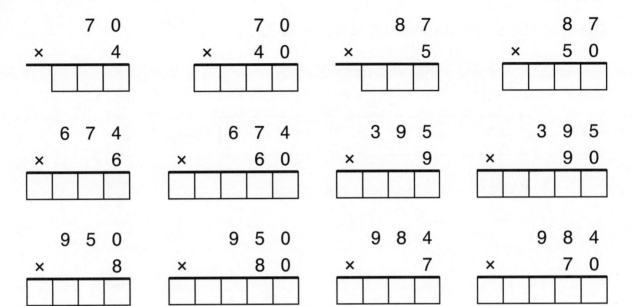

		7	0
×			4

		7	0
×		4	0

		8	7
×			5

		8	7
×		5	0

	6	7	4
×			6

	6	7	4
×		6	0

	3	9	5
×			9

	3	9	5
×		9	0

	9	5	0
×			8

	9	5	0
×		8	0

	9	8	4
×			7

	9	8	4
×		7	0

6 A snail has 33 teeth in 80 rows. How many teeth does the snail have?

7 How many minutes are in 28 hours?

8 How many seconds are in 40 hours?

Basics

1 (a) Estimate the product of 64 and 57.

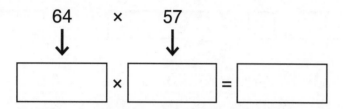

(b) Write the missing numbers or digits.

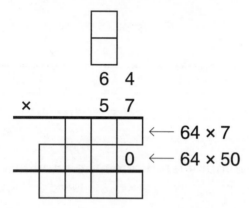

2 (a) Alex estimated the product of 95 and 75 to be 8,000. With what number could he have replaced each factor?

(b) Mei estimated the product of 95 and 75 to be 7,200. With what number could she have replaced each factor?

(c) Whose estimate will be closer to the product?

(d) Find the product of 95 and 75.

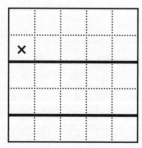

Practice

3 Circle the number that is equal to 47 × 57 without calculating the exact product.

| 1,799 | 3,829 | 2,679 | 279 |

4 Estimate and then find the exact product.

(a) 27 × 85 ≈ ⬚

27 × 85 = ⬚

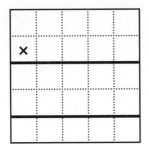

(b) 48 × 48 ≈ ⬚

48 × 48 = ⬚

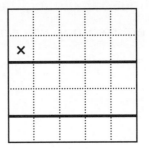

(c) 65 × 72 ≈ ⬚

65 × 72 = ⬚

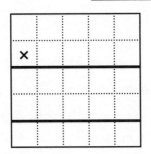

(d) 91 × 38 ≈ ⬚

91 × 38 = ⬚

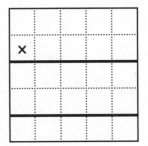

5 24 cookies can be baked on one baking sheet. The cafeteria cook bakes 25 sheets of cookies. Is this enough for 500 people to have at least one cookie?

6 Tickets to the aquarium cost $45 per adult and $35 per child. There are 9 adults and 64 children in a group.

(a) Without calculating the actual cost, determine whether the tickets for the entire group will cost less than $3,000.

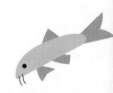

(b) What is the total cost of the tickets for the group?

7 Danios, barbs, and loaches are types of fish that live in Asian rivers. There are 63 danios in an Asian river fish habitat at the aquarium. There are five times as many barbs as danios and three times as many loaches as barbs. How many of these three types of fish are in the habitat?

8 What will be the ones digit in the product of each of the following expressions? Is the product even or odd?

	Ones Digit	Even or Odd
2 × 3		
42 × 33		
5 × 3 × 3		
85 × 33 × 3		

Challenge

9 Find the missing digits.

(a)
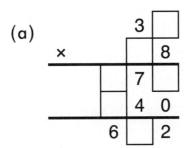

(b)
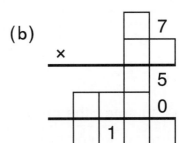

10 Tank A had 3 times as many fish as Tank B. After 240 fish were moved from Tank A to Tank B, Tank A had the same number of fish as Tank B. How many fish are in both tanks altogether?

Basics

1 (a) Estimate the product of 537 and 28.

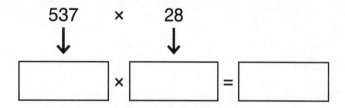

(b) Fill in the missing numbers or digits.

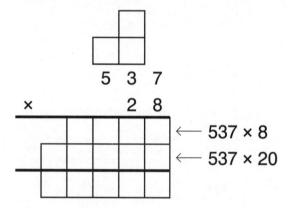

$\longleftarrow$ 537 × 8

$\longleftarrow$ 537 × 20

2 (a) Sofia estimated the product of 649 and 15 to be 12,000. With what numbers could she have replaced each factor?

(b) Emma estimated the product of 649 and 15 to be 13,000. With what numbers could she have replaced each factor?

(c) Whose estimate will be closer to the actual product?

(d) Find the product of 649 and 15.

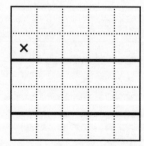

Practice

3 Circle the number that is equal to 845 × 62 without calculating the exact product.

| 56,390 | 5,230 | 52,390 | 25,390 |

4 There are 12 inches in a foot and 5,280 feet in a mile. Which is longer, 50,000 inches or 1 mile?

5 Estimate and then find the exact product.

(a) 638 × 48 ≈ [　　　]

638 × 48 = [　　　]

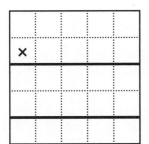

(b) 512 × 72 ≈ [　　　]

512 × 72 = [　　　]

(c) 821 × 58 ≈ [　　　]

821 × 58 = [　　　]

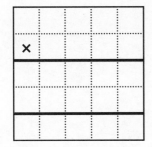

(d) 763 × 65 ≈ [　　　]

763 × 65 = [　　　]

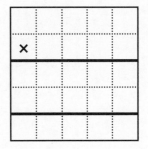

6 Each box contains 275 bandages. There were 14 full boxes and one box that contained 123 bandages. 3 full boxes were used. How many bandages are left?

7 (a) Is the product of 4 × 9 × 7 × 1 odd or even? What is the ones digit of the product?

(b) Is the product of 4 × 419 × 17 × 11 odd or even? What is the ones digit of the product?

8 Write down any 3-digit number. Multiply it by 11. Multiply your answer by 91. What do you notice about your final answer? Try other numbers.

Challenge

9 Find the missing digits.

(a)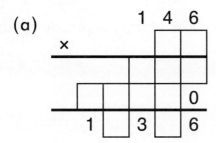

(b)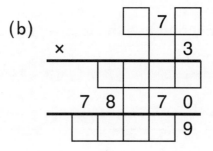

10 Consider the following examples.

$28 \times 25 = 7 \times 4 \times 25 = 7 \times 100 = 700$

$36 \times 50 = 18 \times 2 \times 50 = 18 \times 100 = 1,800$

$18 \times 35 = 9 \times 2 \times 5 \times 7 = 9 \times 7 \times 10 = 630$

Use similar methods to find the following products. Look for factors that together have a product of 10, 100, or 1,000.

(a) $16 \times 25 =$

(b) $25 \times 44 =$

(c) $14 \times 45 =$

(d) $26 \times 15 =$

(e) $75 \times 12 =$

(f) $50 \times 168 =$

(g) $250 \times 36 =$

(h) $125 \times 16 =$

Check

1 Multiply and use the answers to complete the cross number puzzle on the next page.

Across

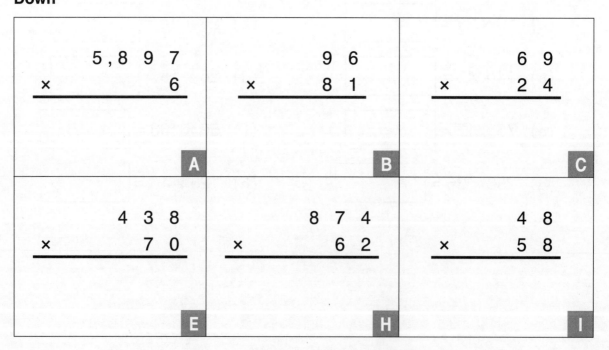

```
      8 6 2
  ×     4 5
  _____
              A
```

```
      7 3 9
  ×     4 2
  _____
              D
```

```
       8 9
  ×     4 2
  _____
              F
```

```
    9,6 0 7
  ×       8
  _____
              G
```

```
      9 8 9
  ×     8 9
  _____
              J
```

```
      7 7 3
  ×     5 8
  _____
              K
```

Down

```
    5,8 9 7
  ×       6
  _____
              A
```

```
       9 6
  ×     8 1
  _____
              B
```

```
       6 9
  ×     2 4
  _____
              C
```

```
      4 3 8
  ×     7 0
  _____
              E
```

```
      8 7 4
  ×     6 2
  _____
              H
```

```
       4 8
  ×     5 8
  _____
              I
```

2 Write > or < in each ◯. Use estimation.

(a) 8,268 × 4 ◯ 32,000

(b) 16 × 84 ◯ 20 × 90

(c) 271 × 12 ◯ 270 × 10

(d) 3,294 × 156 ◯ 3,300 × 160

(e) 6,198 × 4 ◯ 781 × 24

(f) 326 × 21 ◯ 96 × 74

3 Is it possible to multiply a 2-digit whole number by a 2-digit whole number and get a number that is greater than 4 digits? Explain your answer.

4 The pumps and sand filters at the aquarium clean 942 gallons of water a minute. How many gallons do they clean in 45 minutes?

5 One of the buildings at the aquarium is getting new energy-saving light bulbs. Each light fixture holds 4 bulbs. There are 118 light fixtures on each floor. There are 4 floors in the building. How many light bulbs are needed?

6 The aquarium is selling T-shirts at a reduced price of $5 each to celebrate Earth Day. T-shirts are packaged 32 to a box. They ordered 19 boxes of large, 24 boxes of medium, and 22 boxes of small. If they sold all the T-shirts, how much money would they receive?

Challenge

Consecutive numbers are numbers that come one after the other. For example, 3, 4, and 5 are three consecutive whole numbers.

7   What is the ones digit of the product of any 10 consecutive whole numbers?

8   What is the ones digit of the product of any 5 consecutive whole numbers?

9   What are the possible ones digits for the products of any two consecutive whole numbers?

10   The product of 4 consecutive whole numbers is 3,024. What are the numbers?

11 Study the pattern. How many dots will be in the 24th rectangular number?

1st rectangular number	2nd rectangular number	3rd rectangular number	4th rectangular number

4-8 Practice B

Chapter 5 Division

Basics

1 Use mental calculation to find the quotients.

(a) 63 ÷ 3 = [   ]

60   3

(b) 72 ÷ 3 = [   ]

60   12

(c) 55 ÷ 5 = [   ]

50   [ ]

(d) 75 ÷ 5 = [   ]

50   [ ]

(e) 48 ÷ 4 = [   ]

40   [ ]

(f) 68 ÷ 4 = [   ]

40   [ ]

2 (a) 72 ÷ 6 = [   ]

(b) 72 tens ÷ 6 = [   ] tens = [   ]

(c) 72 hundreds ÷ 6 = [   ] hundreds = [   ]

(d) 72 thousands ÷ 6 = [   ] thousands = [   ]

3 (a) 84 ÷ 7 = [   ]

(b) 840 ÷ 7 = [   ]

(c) 8,400 ÷ 7 = [   ]

(d) 84,000 ÷ 7 = [   ]

Practice

 4 Use mental calculation to find the quotients.

(a) 40,000 ÷ 8 = ⬜

(b) 1,500 ÷ 5 = ⬜

(c) 3,600 ÷ 4 = ⬜

(d) 7,200 ÷ 9 = ⬜

(e) 2,400 ÷ 8 = ⬜

(f) 2,700 ÷ 3 = ⬜

(g) 28,000 ÷ 7 = ⬜

(h) 6,400 ÷ 8 = ⬜

(i) 45,000 ÷ 3 = ⬜

(j) 100 ÷ 5 = ⬜

(k) 91,000 ÷ 7 = ⬜

(l) 72,000 ÷ 4 = ⬜

(m) 10,800 ÷ 9 = ⬜

(n) 1,500 ÷ 2 = ⬜

5 A couch costs $360. It costs twice as much as a table. A table costs three times as much as a chair. How much does a chair cost?

6 A factory produced 90,000 jars of jam in 6 hours. If it produces the same number of jars each hour, how many jars does it produce in 2 hours?

Basics

1 (a) Complete the following estimates for the quotient of 743 ÷ 3.

$$600 \div 3 = \boxed{}$$

$$750 \div 3 = \boxed{}$$

$$900 \div 3 = \boxed{}$$

(b) Divide 743 by 3.

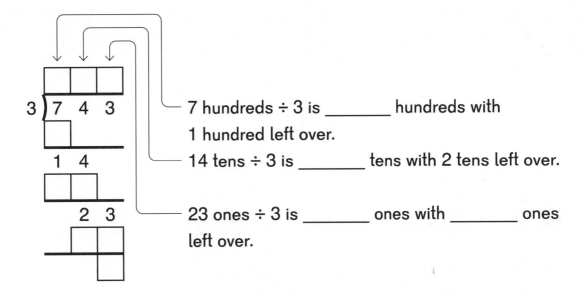

7 hundreds ÷ 3 is _____ hundreds with 1 hundred left over.

14 tens ÷ 3 is _____ tens with 2 tens left over.

23 ones ÷ 3 is _____ ones with _____ ones left over.

743 ÷ 3 is _____ with a remainder of _____.

(c) Compare the estimates to the actual quotient. Which estimate(s) were lower? Which estimate(s) were higher? Which estimate was closest?

(d) Check: $\boxed{} \times 3 + \boxed{} = 743$

Practice

2 (a) Emma's estimate: $878 \div 9 \approx 900 \div 9$

Alex's estimate: $878 \div 9 \approx 880 \div 10$

Mei's estimate: $878 \div 9 \approx 810 \div 9$

List the estimates in order from least to greatest.

(b) Divide 878 by 9.

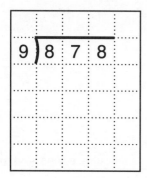

3 Which of the following gives the greatest quotient? Circle it.

653 ÷ 7		700 ÷ 8		498 ÷ 5

4 A community boating center had $200. It bought 6 identical life vests for its customers to use and had $8 left. Using estimation, circle the most reasonable cost for each life vest.

$21		$32		$48

5 (a) Estimate and then divide.

$848 \div 3 \approx$ [　　]

$972 \div 4 \approx$ [　　]

$715 \div 2 \approx$ [　　]

$$3 \overline{)8 \; 4 \; 8}$$

$$4 \overline{)9 \; 7 \; 2}$$

$$2 \overline{)7 \; 1 \; 5}$$

$625 \div 7 \approx$ [　　]

$556 \div 8 \approx$ [　　]

$828 \div 4 \approx$ [　　]

$$7 \overline{)6 \; 2 \; 5}$$

$$8 \overline{)5 \; 5 \; 6}$$

$$4 \overline{)8 \; 2 \; 8}$$

(b) Put the quotients in order from least to greatest. Add the middle two numbers. Divide that answer by the sum of the remainders. You will get 50 if you did all the calculations correctly.

6 At a fair, balloons were given out in this order: yellow, blue, blue, red, red, red, yellow, blue, blue, red, red, red, and so on until 250 balloons were given out.

(a) What color was the 250th balloon?

(b) How many red balloons were given out?

Challenge

7 (a) Find the remainder of 68 ÷ 9.

Find the remainder of 69 ÷ 9.

Find the remainder of the sum of the two remainders divided by 9.

Find the remainder of 68 + 69 divided by 9.

What do you notice? Try it with some other numbers.

(b) Find the remainder when 17 + 15 + 11 is divided by 4.

(c) Find the remainder when 69 + 69 + 74 + 58 is divided by 8.

Basics

1 (a) Complete the following estimations for the quotient of 9,875 ÷ 4.

8,000 ÷ 4 = ☐

10,000 ÷ 4 = ☐

12,000 ÷ 4 = ☐

(b) Divide 9,875 by 4.

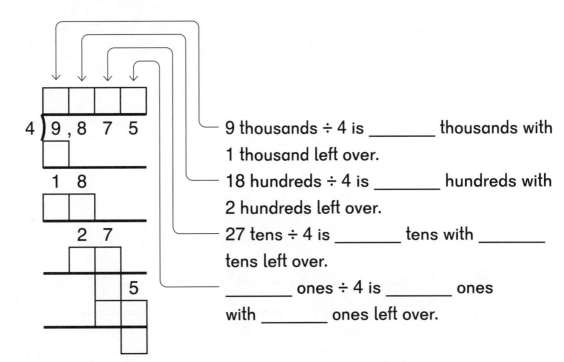

4) 9 , 8 7 5

1 8

2 7

5

9 thousands ÷ 4 is _____ thousands with 1 thousand left over.

18 hundreds ÷ 4 is _____ hundreds with 2 hundreds left over.

27 tens ÷ 4 is _____ tens with _____ tens left over.

_____ ones ÷ 4 is _____ ones with _____ ones left over.

9,875 ÷ 4 is _____ with a remainder of _____.

(c) Compare the estimates to the actual quotient. Which estimate(s) were lower? Which estimate(s) were higher? Which estimate was closest?

(d) Check: ☐ × 4 + ☐ = 9,875

Practice

2 (a) Sofia's estimate: $4{,}975 \div 3 \approx 3{,}000 \div 3$

Mei's estimate: $4{,}975 \div 3 \approx 6{,}000 \div 3$

Dion's estimate: $4{,}975 \div 3 \approx 4{,}500 \div 3$

List the estimates in order from least to greatest.

(b) Divide 4,975 by 3.

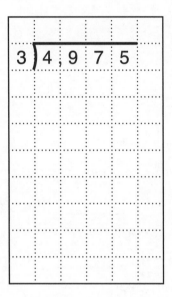

3 $6{,}798 \div 5$ is closest to which number? Circle it.

| 150 | 1,000 | 1,500 | 2,000 |

4 Two of these expressions have the same quotient. Circle them.

| 4,950 ÷ 6 | 6,531 ÷ 7 | 3,780 ÷ 5 | 2,799 ÷ 3 |

5 Is the quotient of $7{,}489 \div 8$ three or four digits?

6 **(a)** Estimate and then divide.

8,375 ÷ 6 ≈ [   ]   9,971 ÷ 2 ≈ [   ]

```
6 ) 8,3 7 5
```

```
2 ) 9,9 7 1
```

7,761 ÷ 9 ≈ [   ]   3,945 ÷ 5 ≈ [   ]

```
9 ) 7,7 6 1
```

```
5 ) 3,9 4 5
```

(b) Add the quotients and the remainders together, then divide that sum by 5. You will get 1,608 if you did all the calculations correctly.

7 How many egg cartons are needed for 2,560 eggs if each carton holds 6 eggs?

8 Students are seated in the following order on a train: 1= left window, 2 = left aisle, 3 = right aisle, 4 = right window, 5 = left window, etc. Jacob gets seat 1,423. Where is his seat?

left window	left aisle		right aisle	right window

Challenge

9 Find the missing numbers.

(a)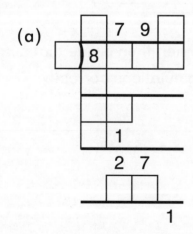

(b)

Check

1 Use mental calculation to find the quotients.

(a) $2,000 \div 5 =$ ⬚

(b) $560 \div 8 =$ ⬚

(c) $90,000 \div 6 =$ ⬚

(d) $15,000 \div 2 =$ ⬚

(e) $6,400 \div 4 =$ ⬚

(f) $75,000 \div 3 =$ ⬚

2 Circle the number that is equal to $6,461 \div 7$. Use estimation.

| 795 | 893 | 923 | 1,373 |

3 Two of these expressions have the same quotient. Circle them.

| $598 \div 6$ | $1,400 \div 8$ | $875 \div 5$ | $4,007 \div 3$ |

4 Write > or < in each ◯. Use estimation.

(a) $8,268 \div 4 \bigcirc 2,000$

(b) $842 \div 7 \bigcirc 276 \div 2$

(c) $3,824 \div 9 \bigcirc 4,000 \div 8$

(d) $5,723 \div 6 \bigcirc 4,789 \div 4$

(e) $9,199 \div 3 \bigcirc 587 \times 4$

(f) $7,155 \div 8 \bigcirc 528 + 679$

5 (a) Divide.

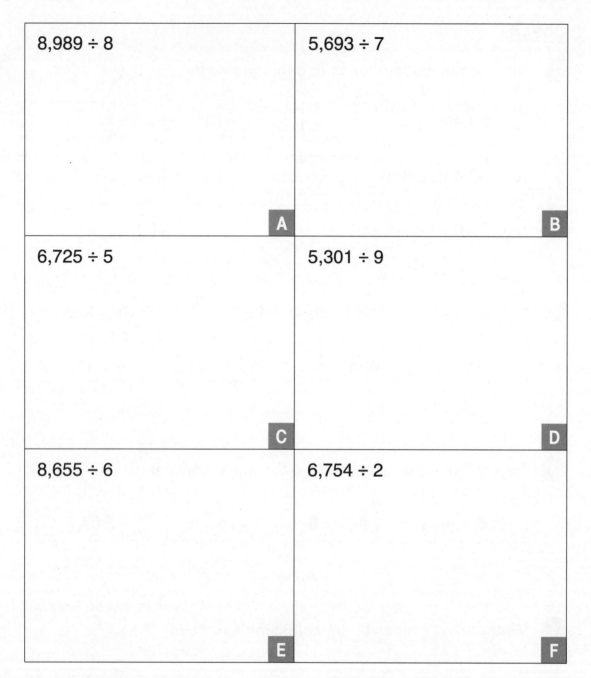

8,989 ÷ 8 **A**	5,693 ÷ 7 **B**
6,725 ÷ 5 **C**	5,301 ÷ 9 **D**
8,655 ÷ 6 **E**	6,754 ÷ 2 **F**

(b) Write the digits of the answers and the remainders from problems A to F in order below. Add consecutive numbers together. If you did all the calculations correctly, you will discover a pattern.

☐, ☐, ☐, ☐, ☐, ☐, ☐ , ☐ , ☐ ,

☐ , ☐ , ☐ , ☐ , ☐ ...

6 6 kayak paddles cost $348. What is the cost of 1 kayak paddle?

7 A 5-person pedal boat costs 5 times as much as a stand-up paddle board. If the pedal boat costs $1,245, how much does the paddle board cost?

8 A community boating center had $2,000. It bought 8 identical kayaks and had $8 left. How much did each kayak cost?

Challenge

9 Mei plays a game with coins. She puts 4 coins in a row, heads up. In the first move, she turns over the first coin. In the second move, she turns over the first two coins. In the third move, she turns over the first three coins. In the fourth move, she turns over all four coins. In the fifth move, she starts over again, turning over the first coin. And so on. What side of each coin is facing up after 1,995 moves?

Starting position	H	H	H	H
1st move	T	H	H	H
2nd move	H	T	H	H
3rd move	T	H	T	H

...

5-4 Practice A

Basics

1 There are 3 neighboring orchards, A, B, and C. Orchard A has 60 fewer fruit trees than Orchard B. Orchard C has 3 times as many fruit trees as Orchard B. If the three orchards have 430 fruit trees altogether, how many fruit trees does Orchard C have?

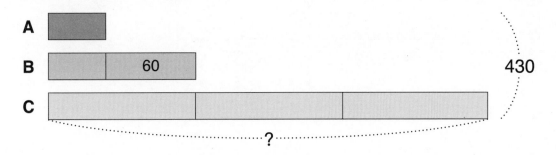

2 There are 3 neighboring orchards, D, E, and F. Orchard D has 60 fewer fruit trees than Orchard E. Orchard D has 3 times as many fruit trees as Orchard F. If the three orchards have 424 fruit trees altogether, how many fruit trees does Orchard F have?

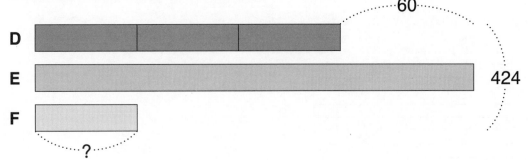

3 There are 3 neighboring orchards, K, L, and M. Orchard K has 4 times as many fruit trees as Orchard L. Orchard M has 60 fewer fruit trees than Orchard K. If Orchards K and L together have 430 fruit trees, how many fruit trees does Orchard M have?

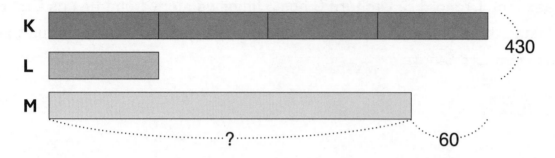

4 A paddle for adults costs $10 more than a paddle for kids. The boating center bought 4 of each type of paddle. The total cost was $312. What was the total cost for 4 adult-sized paddles?

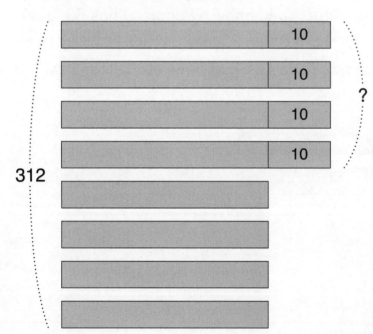

Practice

5 Three siblings bought a small sailboat together. The sailboat cost $3,150. Ada contributed $20 more than Bron. Cora contributed $130 less than twice as much money as Ada. How much money did Bron contribute?

6 A community boating center had $12,500. It bought 3 surf skis and 1 keelboat and had $265 left over. The keelboat cost $6,455 more than a surf ski. How much did the keelboat cost?

7 An apartment complex manager is replacing some of the appliances. He bought 3 ovens and 4 refrigerators for $4,583. Each oven cost $570 less than a refrigerator. What is the cost of one oven?

8 A factory produced 3,460 jars of jam. It produced 3 times as many jars of strawberry jam as apricot jam, 60 more jars of plum jam than apricot jam, and 140 fewer jars of peach jam than apricot jam. How many jars of peach jam did it produce?

Basics

1 In a car sales lot there were three times as many vans as sedans. After 105 vans were sold, there were twice as many sedans as vans. How many cars were there in the end?

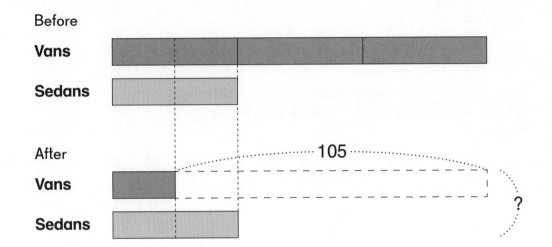

Before

Vans

Sedans

After

Vans

Sedans

105

?

2 A box of toy cars has 96 more red cars than blue cars. After 20 blue cars were added, it had 3 times as many red cars as blue cars. How many cars were there in the end?

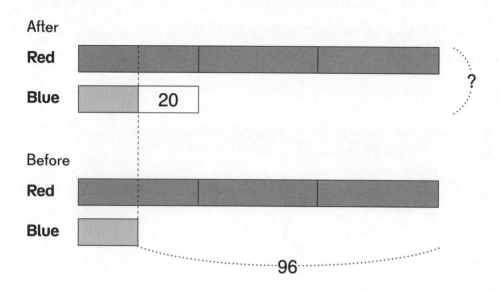

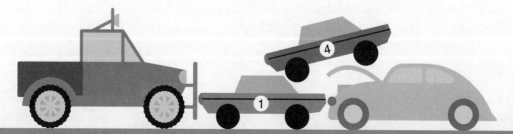

Practice

3 2 fish tanks, A and B, had a total of 196 fish. Tank A has more fish than Tank B. After 32 fish were added to Tank A and 15 fish in Tank B were sold, Tank A had 75 more fish than Tank B. How many fish did each tank have at first?

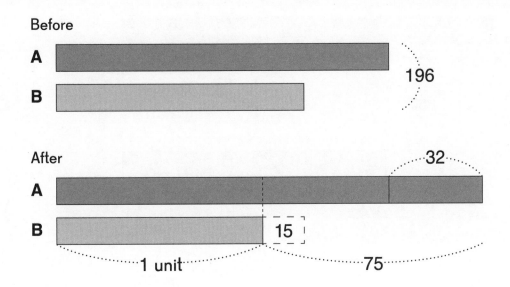

Total number of fish after:

Value of 1 unit:

Number of fish in Tank A at first:

Number of fish in Tank B at first:

4 Dorothy has $900 and Maria has $360. They each bought a couch at the same price. Now, Dorothy has 7 times as much money as Maria. How much did the couch cost?

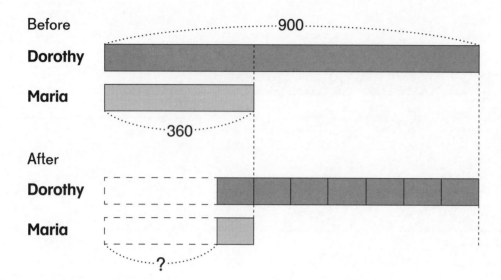

Before

Dorothy

Maria

900

360

After

Dorothy

Maria

?

5 Daren saved 7 times as much money as Matt. They both saved another $370. Now they have $900 altogether. How much money has Daren saved?

Check

1 Divide.

(a) 9,886 ÷ 6   (b) 4,009 ÷ 7

2 The sum of three numbers is 1,349. The greatest number is three times the least number. The third number is 133 less than twice the least number. What are the three numbers?

3 A boating center rents out dinghies, kayaks, and keelboats for 4 hours. The cost for renting a dinghy is $30 more than the cost of renting a kayak. A group rented 3 dinghies and 2 kayaks. The total cost was $315. What is the cost for renting a kayak?

4 A bin has 382 red, yellow, blue, and green balls. It has three times as many red balls as yellow balls, 52 more blue balls than yellow balls, and 30 fewer green balls than red balls. How many green balls does it have?

5 Cody wants to buy some apple trees for his property. He needs $48 more to buy 3 apple trees. After getting $240 more, he had enough money to buy 5 apple trees. How much does 1 apple tree cost?

6 A number with the hundreds digit of 3 and tens digit of 2 is divided by 9. The remainder is 5. What is the ones digit of the number?

Check

Number	Rounded to the nearest			
	100,000	10,000	1,000	100
134,710				
634,550				
98,432				
250,500				

2. The number 83,238 is a palindrome. It is the same read from left to right and from right to left (ignoring the comma). What is the 10th palindrome after 83,238?

3. Use the clues to find the mystery 6-digit number.

Clue 1 All the digits are different.
Clue 2 The digit 9 is in the ten thousands place.
Clue 3 The digit in the hundreds place is 6 less than the digit in the ten thousands place.
Clue 4 One of the digits stands for 5,000.
Clue 5 The number is less than 200,000.
Clue 6 The digit in the tens place stands for 0.
Clue 7 The number is an odd number.

4 Use estimation to arrange the expressions in order from least to greatest.

(a)

32 × 76	846 + 1,158	8,462 − 4,981	178 × 8
A	B	C	D

(b)

16,982 + 33,174	756 × 72	409,563 − 343,669
A	B	C

5 List all the common factors of 30 and 45.

6 List the first four common multiples of 3, 4, and 6.

7 (a) Can the sum of two prime numbers be an odd number? Explain why or why not.

(b) Can the product of two prime numbers be an odd number? Explain why or why not.

8 A 2-digit odd number is a factor of 60 and a multiple of 3. What is the number?

9 Use the clues to determine which number, 61, 23, 72, or 51, is on the other side of the cards A, B, C, and D.

Clue 1 A prime number is between two composite numbers.
Clue 2 The odd multiple of 3 has no card to the right of it.
Clue 3 The least number is not between two cards.

A	B	C	D

10 A community boating center had 3 fundraisers last year for their youth sailing program. At the first fundraiser, they raised $18,945. At the second fundraiser, they raised $7,285 more than at the first fundraiser. At the third fundraiser, they raised $5,982 less than at the second fundraiser. How much money did they raise in all?

11 A vendor at a farmers market is selling honey. He has 1,450 jars in total of alfalfa, blueberry, and clover honey. He has 130 more jars of alfalfa honey than blueberry honey. He has twice as many jars of clover honey as alfalfa honey. How many jars of alfalfa honey does he have?

12 3 ships leave a port on January 31. The first one returns to the port every 4 weeks, the second one every 8 weeks, and the third one every 10 weeks. In how many weeks will they all be in the port again?

13 Oliver had 3 times as many rocks in his collection as Katie. Then Oliver collected 75 more rocks and Katie collected 105 more rocks. Now Katie has the same number of rocks as Oliver. How many rocks did Oliver have at first?

Challenge

14 This year, John's age is a multiple of 3. Last year, his age was 1 less than a multiple of 4. Next year, his age will be 3 more than a multiple of 5. What is the youngest age he could be?

15 In a textbook, 900 digits are used for the page numbers. How many pages are in the textbook, starting with page 1? (Hint: First find how many digits are used for pages 1-9 and 10-99.)

Chapter 6 Fractions

Basics

1 Write the equivalent fractions.

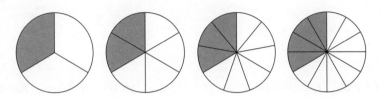

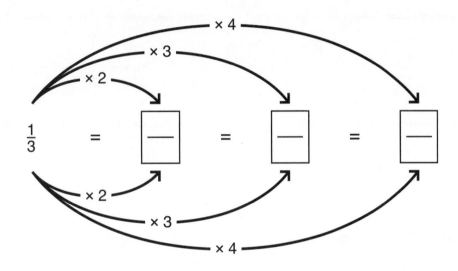

$$\frac{1}{3} = \boxed{} = \boxed{} = \boxed{}$$

2 Simplify the fractions.

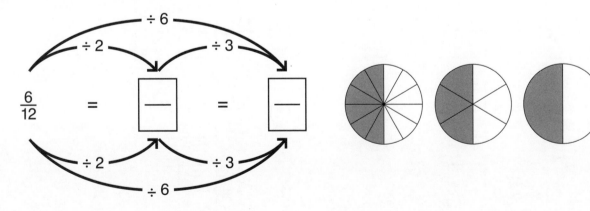

$$\frac{6}{12} = \boxed{} = \boxed{}$$

The simplest form of $\frac{6}{12}$ is $\boxed{}$.

Practice

3 Write the missing numbers for the fraction indicated by the arrow.

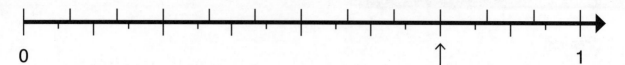

0   ↑   1

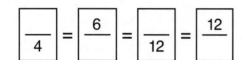

$$\frac{}{4} = \frac{6}{} = \frac{}{12} = \frac{12}{}$$

4 Label the tick marks indicated by the arrows as fractions in simplest form.

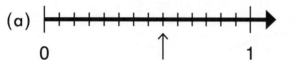

(a)   0   ↑   1   (b)   0   ↑   1

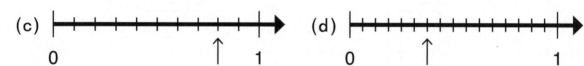

(c)   0   ↑   1   (d)   0   ↑   1

5 Express each fraction in simplest form.

(a) $\frac{6}{9} = \boxed{}$ (b) $\frac{6}{8} = \boxed{}$

(c) $\frac{6}{15} = \boxed{}$ (d) $\frac{10}{12} = \boxed{}$

(e) $\frac{21}{42} = \boxed{}$ (f) $\frac{24}{32} = \boxed{}$

(g) $\frac{42}{56} = \boxed{}$ (h) $\frac{18}{72} = \boxed{}$

6 Write the missing numbers.

(a) $\dfrac{28}{42} = \dfrac{}{21} = \dfrac{2}{} = \dfrac{}{9} = \dfrac{18}{}$

(b) $\dfrac{75}{100} = \dfrac{}{20} = \dfrac{3}{} = \dfrac{}{12} = \dfrac{}{36}$

7 Find the equivalent fractions.

(a) $\dfrac{5}{10} = \dfrac{1}{}$

(b) $\dfrac{1}{2} = \dfrac{}{16}$

(c) $\dfrac{5}{10} = \dfrac{8}{}$

(d) $\dfrac{6}{9} = \dfrac{}{3}$

(e) $\dfrac{2}{3} = \dfrac{8}{}$

(f) $\dfrac{6}{9} = \dfrac{}{12}$

(g) $\dfrac{6}{8} = \dfrac{3}{}$

(h) $\dfrac{3}{4} = \dfrac{9}{}$

(i) $\dfrac{6}{8} = \dfrac{9}{}$

(j) $\dfrac{8}{10} = \dfrac{}{5}$

(k) $\dfrac{12}{15} = \dfrac{}{5}$

(l) $\dfrac{8}{10} = \dfrac{}{15}$

(m) $\dfrac{3}{6} = \dfrac{}{8}$

(n) $\dfrac{12}{16} = \dfrac{15}{}$

(o) $\dfrac{24}{30} = \dfrac{}{20}$

Challenge

8 The fractions below form a number pattern. What is the missing fraction?

$\dfrac{5}{12}, \dfrac{1}{2}, \boxed{}, \dfrac{2}{3}, \dfrac{3}{4}$

Basics

1 Write > or < in each ◯.

(a) $\frac{5}{12}$ ◯ $\frac{7}{12}$

(b) $\frac{5}{12}$ ◯ $\frac{5}{9}$

2 Label the correct tick marks for the given fractions on the number lines. Then find equivalent fractions. Write > or < in each ◯.

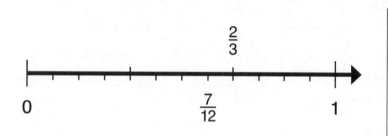

$\frac{2}{3} = \boxed{\dfrac{}{12}}$

$\frac{7}{12}$

$\frac{2}{3}$ ◯ $\frac{7}{12}$

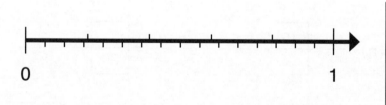

$\frac{3}{5} = \boxed{\dfrac{9}{}}$

$\frac{9}{16}$

$\frac{3}{5}$ ◯ $\frac{9}{16}$

$\frac{2}{5} = \boxed{\dfrac{}{}}$

$\frac{3}{7} = \boxed{\dfrac{}{}}$

$\frac{2}{5}$ ◯ $\frac{3}{7}$

3 Write >, <, or = in each ◯.

(a) $\frac{4}{8}$◯$\frac{1}{2}$ | $\frac{5}{8}$◯$\frac{1}{2}$ | $\frac{3}{8}$◯$\frac{1}{2}$

(b) $\frac{6}{12}$◯$\frac{1}{2}$ | $\frac{6}{13}$◯$\frac{1}{2}$ | $\frac{6}{11}$◯$\frac{1}{2}$

(c) $\frac{6}{13}$◯$\frac{5}{8}$ | $\frac{6}{11}$◯$\frac{3}{8}$

4 (a) Label $\frac{4}{5}$ and $\frac{6}{7}$ on the number line.

0   1

(b) $\frac{4}{5}$ and $\boxed{\frac{}{5}}$ make 1. | $\frac{6}{7}$ and $\boxed{\frac{}{7}}$ make 1.

(c) Which fraction is closer to 1?

Which fraction is greater?

Practice

5 Write > or < in each ◯.

(a) $\frac{7}{8}$◯$\frac{3}{4}$ (b) $\frac{3}{5}$◯$\frac{7}{15}$

(c) $\frac{4}{7}$◯$\frac{8}{9}$ (d) $\frac{3}{4}$◯$\frac{9}{11}$

(e) $\frac{2}{3}$◯$\frac{3}{8}$ (f) $\frac{5}{12}$◯$\frac{7}{16}$

(g) $\frac{10}{11}$◯$\frac{8}{9}$ (h) $\frac{15}{16}$◯$\frac{10}{11}$

6 Circle the fractions that are less than $\frac{1}{2}$. Then write the fractions in order from least to greatest.

$$\frac{3}{8} \qquad \frac{8}{11} \qquad \frac{3}{5} \qquad \frac{5}{16} \qquad \frac{8}{15} \qquad \frac{5}{12}$$

7 Write the fractions in order from least to greatest.

(a) $\frac{5}{6}, \frac{6}{7}, \frac{3}{5}$

(b) $\frac{8}{9}, \frac{23}{50}, \frac{12}{13}$

(c) $\frac{13}{16}, \frac{2}{5}, \frac{5}{8}, \frac{7}{7}$

(d) $\frac{7}{12}, \frac{3}{7}, \frac{5}{14}, \frac{31}{48}$

Challenge

8 Use the given numbers to fill in the missing numerators or denominators so that the fractions are in order from least to greatest. Each fraction should be less than 1 and in simplest form.

(a) 5, 6, 7, 8

$$\boxed{\dfrac{3}{}} < \boxed{\dfrac{}{12}} < \boxed{\dfrac{}{}}$$

(b) 7, 8, 9, 10, 11, 12

$$\boxed{\dfrac{}{}} < \boxed{\dfrac{}{}} < \boxed{\dfrac{}{}}$$

Basics

1 Write an improper fraction for each of the following.

(a)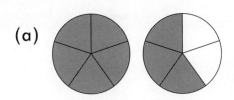

8 fifths = $\dfrac{\boxed{}}{5}$

(b)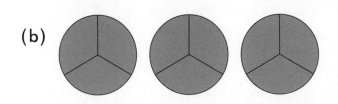

9 thirds = $\dfrac{\boxed{}}{3}$

(c)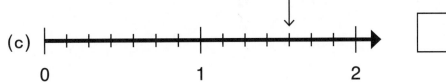

 $\boxed{}$ sevenths = $\dfrac{\boxed{}}{\boxed{}}$

2 Write a mixed number for each of the following.

(a)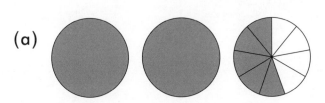

$2 + \dfrac{5}{9} = 2\dfrac{\boxed{}}{9}$

(b)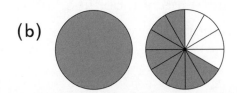

$1 + \dfrac{\boxed{}}{12} = 1\dfrac{\boxed{}}{3}$

(c)

$3 + \dfrac{\boxed{}}{\boxed{}} = \boxed{}\dfrac{\boxed{}}{\boxed{}}$

Practice

3 Express each of the following as a mixed number and as an improper fraction in simplest form.

	Mixed Number	Improper Fraction
1 whole		
1 whole		
1 whole		

4 Finish labeling each arrow with a fraction above the number line and a mixed number below the number line. Use simplest form.

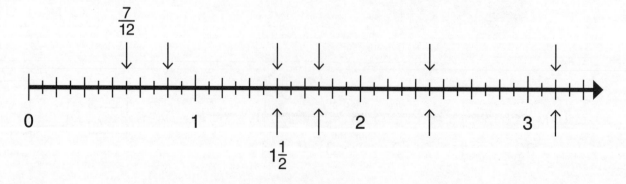

5 Write the length of each line in centimeters as both a mixed number and a fraction. Use simplest form.

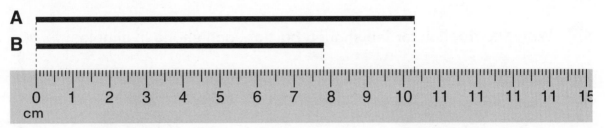

A

B

6 Write a mixed number for each of the following.

(a)

$$3 - \frac{1}{5} = 2 \boxed{}$$

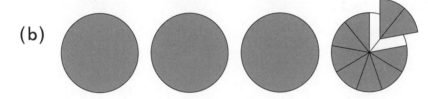

(b)

$$4 - \frac{2}{9} = \boxed{}\boxed{}$$

7 Express each value as a mixed number in simplest form.

(a) $3 + \frac{2}{3}$

(b) $4 - \frac{4}{9}$

(c) $5 + \frac{6}{8}$

(d) $8 - \frac{6}{12}$

(e) $\frac{8}{14} + 8$

(f) $3 - \frac{7}{15}$

Check

1 Write the fraction for the shaded part of each shape in simplest form.

(a) 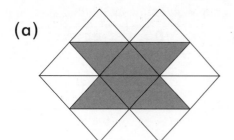  (b)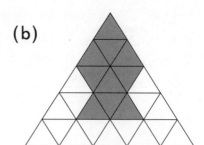

2 Which fractions are greater than 1?

$\dfrac{8}{5}$ $\quad$ $\dfrac{7}{16}$ $\quad$ $\dfrac{11}{9}$ $\quad$ $\dfrac{15}{13}$ $\quad$ $\dfrac{6}{15}$

3 Which fraction is closest to 1?

$\dfrac{3}{4}$ $\quad$ $\dfrac{1}{2}$ $\quad$ $\dfrac{4}{5}$ $\quad$ $\dfrac{5}{6}$ $\quad$ $\dfrac{2}{3}$

4 Write > or < in each $\bigcirc$.

(a) $\dfrac{5}{8} \bigcirc \dfrac{8}{5}$ $\qquad$ (b) $2\dfrac{3}{5} \bigcirc 2\dfrac{7}{15}$ $\qquad$ (c) $\dfrac{11}{8} \bigcirc \dfrac{5}{4}$

5 In a relay race, Aisha ran $1\dfrac{3}{4}$ of a mile and Paula ran $1\dfrac{5}{12}$ of a mile. Who ran farther?

6 Label each arrow with a fraction above the number line and a mixed number below the number line. Use simplest form.

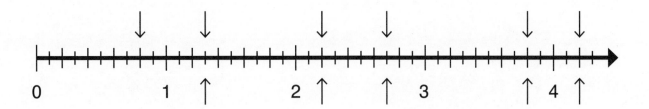

7 Label the tick marks on the number line with the given numbers.

$3\frac{3}{10}$, $2\frac{2}{5}$, $\frac{1}{2}$, $1\frac{1}{3}$, $\frac{9}{12}$, $3\frac{7}{14}$, $1\frac{5}{7}$, $2\frac{6}{8}$

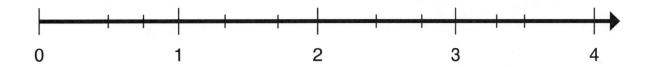

8 Write the missing numerators or denominators. Each fraction should be in simplest form.

(a) $\frac{2}{9} < \boxed{\dfrac{1}{}} < \frac{2}{7}$

(b) $\frac{1}{2} < \boxed{\dfrac{3}{}} < \frac{3}{4}$

(c) $\frac{3}{4} < \boxed{\dfrac{}{5}} < 1$

(d) $2\frac{2}{3} < 2\boxed{\dfrac{8}{}} < 2\frac{4}{5}$

Challenge

9 List all the different fractions between 0 and 1 that are in simplest form where the denominators are 10 or less.

10 (a) How many more squares need to be shaded in order to have $\frac{4}{9}$ of the rectangle unshaded?

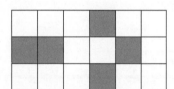

(b) How many more squares need to be shaded in order to have $\frac{1}{4}$ of the rectangle unshaded?

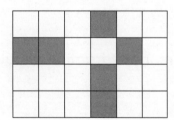

(c) How many more squares need to be shaded in order to have $1\frac{2}{3}$ unshaded?

1 whole

Basics

1 (a) Express $\frac{15}{4}$ as a mixed number.

 $= 1$ $\boxed{\frac{}{4}} = 2$ $\boxed{\frac{}{4}} = 3$

$\frac{15}{4} = \frac{12}{4} + \frac{3}{4}$

$\phantom{\frac{15}{4}} = 3 + \frac{3}{4}$

$\phantom{\frac{15}{4}} =$

(b) Express $\frac{23}{9}$ as a mixed number.

$\boxed{\frac{}{9}} = 1$ $\boxed{\frac{}{9}} = 2$

$\frac{23}{9} = \boxed{\frac{}{9}} + \boxed{\frac{}{9}}$

$\phantom{\frac{23}{9}} = 2 + \boxed{\frac{}{9}}$

$\phantom{\frac{23}{9}} =$

Practice

2 Label each arrow with a mixed number in simplest form or a whole number.

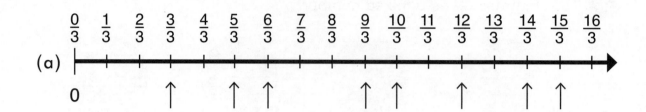

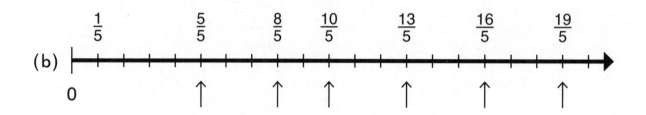

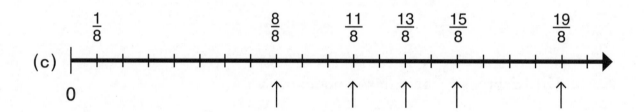

3 Express each improper fraction as a whole number.

(a) $\frac{15}{5}$ (b) $\frac{90}{9}$

(c) $\frac{24}{2}$ (d) $\frac{40}{8}$

(e) $\frac{54}{6}$ (f) $\frac{56}{7}$

4 Express each improper fraction as a mixed number in simplest form.

(a) $\frac{18}{4} = \frac{16}{4} + \frac{2}{4}$

=

(b) $\frac{27}{5} = \frac{25}{5} + \frac{2}{5}$

=

(c) $\frac{16}{7} =$

=

(d) $\frac{9}{4} =$

=

(e) $\frac{20}{6} =$

=

(f) $\frac{11}{2} =$

=

(g) $\frac{20}{8} =$

=

(h) $\frac{30}{9} =$

=

5 Write the following numbers in order from least to greatest.

$\frac{18}{5}, \frac{23}{7}, \frac{14}{3}$

Basics

1 (a) Express $3\frac{2}{3}$ as an improper fraction.

$1 = \frac{3}{3}$ $2 = \frac{6}{3}$ $3 = \frac{\boxed{}}{3}$

$$3\frac{2}{3} \;=\; 3 + \frac{2}{3}$$

$$=\; \frac{9}{3} + \frac{2}{3}$$

$$=$$

(b) Express $2\frac{5}{8}$ as an improper fraction.

$1 = \dfrac{\boxed{}}{8}$ $2 = \dfrac{\boxed{}}{8}$

$$2\frac{5}{8} = 2 + \frac{\boxed{}}{8}$$

$$=\; \frac{\boxed{}}{8} + \frac{\boxed{}}{8}$$

$$=$$

Practice

2 Label each arrow with an improper fraction with a denominator of 4.

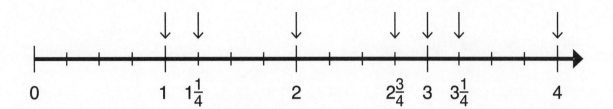

3 Label each arrow with an improper fraction.

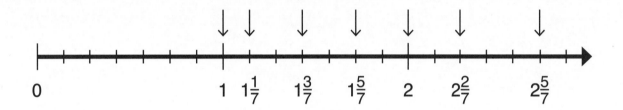

4 Express each whole number as an improper fraction with the given denominator.

(a) $2 = \dfrac{}{9}$

(b) $3 = \dfrac{}{8}$

(c) $4 = \dfrac{}{5}$

(d) $5 = \dfrac{}{3}$

(e) $4 = \dfrac{}{12}$

(f) $8 = \dfrac{}{16}$

5 Express each value as an improper fraction.

(a) $3\frac{2}{5} = \frac{15}{5} + \frac{2}{5}$

$= \qquad$

(b) $5\frac{2}{9} = \frac{45}{9} + \frac{2}{9}$

$= \qquad$

(c) $4\frac{5}{6} = \qquad$

$= \qquad$

(d) $7\frac{1}{7} = \qquad$

$= \qquad$

(e) $5\frac{7}{10} = \qquad$

$= \qquad$

(f) $6\frac{5}{8} = \qquad$

$= \qquad$

(g) $2\frac{5}{12} = \qquad$

$= \qquad$

(h) $11\frac{2}{3} = \qquad$

$= \qquad$

6 Write the following numbers in order from least to greatest.

$\frac{14}{3}, 3\frac{3}{7}, \frac{21}{4}$

Basics

1 (a) Divide 2 by 5. Write the answer as a fraction.

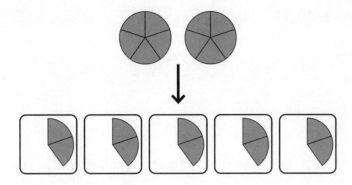

$$2 \div 5 = \boxed{}$$

(b) Divide 7 by 5. Write the answer as a mixed number.

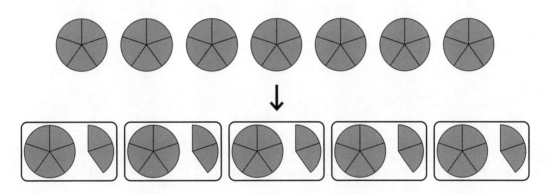

$$7 \div 5 = \boxed{} \boxed{}$$

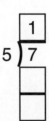

2 (a) Divide 2 by 4. Write the answer as a fraction in simplest form.

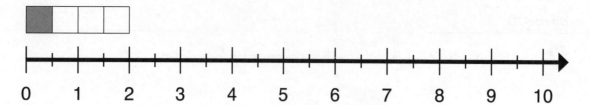

$2 \div 4 = \frac{2}{4} = \boxed{\frac{}{2}}$

(b) Divide 10 by 4. Write the answer as a mixed number in simplest form.

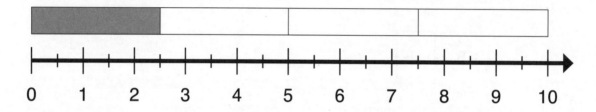

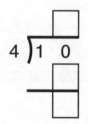

$10 \div 4 = \boxed{} \boxed{\frac{}{4}} = \boxed{} \boxed{\frac{}{2}}$

3 Express each improper fraction as a mixed number in simplest form.

(a) $\frac{50}{7} = 50 \div 7$ 7)5 0

(b) $\frac{56}{6} = 56 \div 6$ 6)5 6

=

=

Practice

4 Divide. Express answers 1 or greater as whole or mixed numbers. Use simplest form.

(a) $3 \div 7$

(b) $8 \div 10$

(c) $\frac{45}{3}$

(d) $31 \div 9$

(e) $32 \div 6$

(f) $49 \div 5$

(g) $\frac{45}{4}$

(h) $79 \div 5$

5 A 38 oz box of cereal has 8 servings. How many ounces are in each serving?

Check

1 Express each mixed number as an improper fraction.

(a) $9\frac{1}{2}$

(b) $6\frac{2}{3}$

(c) $10\frac{5}{6}$

(d) $8\frac{4}{9}$

2 Express each value as a whole number or mixed number in simplest form.

(a) $\frac{25}{2}$

(b) $\frac{51}{7}$

(c) $\frac{46}{4}$

(d) $\frac{40}{3}$

(e) $46 \div 8$

(f) $85 \div 9$

3 45 pounds of rice is divided equally into 6 bags. How many pounds of rice are in each bag?

4 Continue the patterns. Express numbers 1 or greater as whole or mixed numbers. Use simplest form.

(a) Count on by three fourths starting with $\frac{1}{4}$.

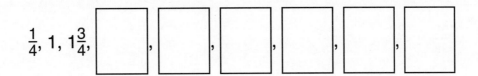

$\frac{1}{4}$, 1, $1\frac{3}{4}$, ☐ , ☐ , ☐ , ☐ , ☐ , ☐

(b) Count on by three eighths starting with $\frac{1}{8}$.

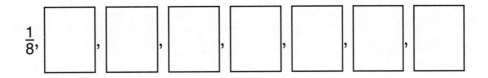

$\frac{1}{8}$, ☐ , ☐ , ☐ , ☐ , ☐ , ☐

(c) Count on by two ninths starting with $\frac{2}{9}$.

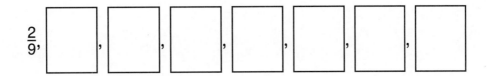

$\frac{2}{9}$, ☐ , ☐ , ☐ , ☐ , ☐ , ☐

5 Write the numbers in order from least to greatest.

(a) $\frac{16}{3}$, $4\frac{7}{8}$, $\frac{26}{6}$

(b) $\frac{42}{10}$, $\frac{60}{9}$, $\frac{52}{7}$, $\frac{28}{5}$

6 (a) Which fraction is closest to 5?

$$\frac{14}{3} \qquad \frac{19}{4} \qquad \frac{11}{5} \qquad \frac{43}{8}$$

(b) Which fraction is closest to 10?

$$\frac{59}{6} \qquad \frac{50}{4} \qquad \frac{68}{7} \qquad \frac{78}{8}$$

7 Write the whole numbers that are between $\frac{19}{3}$ and $\frac{47}{4}$.

Challenge

8 One half is one third of what mixed number?

9 Two lumps of clay weigh the same. If you put 1 lump of clay on one side of a balance, and $\frac{3}{5}$ of the second lump of clay along with a $\frac{1}{2}$ kg weight on the other side of the balance, the two sides are balanced. How much does a lump of clay weigh?

Chapter 7 Adding and Subtracting Fractions

Basics

1 (a) Add $\frac{5}{8}$ and $\frac{7}{8}$.

$$\frac{5}{8} + \frac{7}{8} = \boxed{\frac{}{8}}$$

$$= 1\boxed{\frac{}{8}}$$

$$= 1\boxed{\frac{}{2}}$$

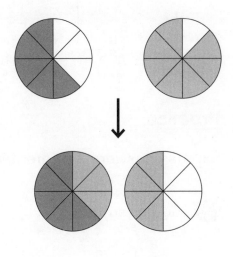

(b) Subtract $\frac{5}{8}$ from $\frac{7}{8}$.

$$\frac{7}{8} - \frac{5}{8} = \boxed{\frac{}{8}}$$

$$= \boxed{\frac{}{4}}$$

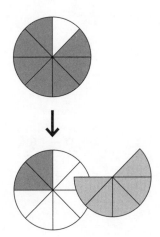

2 Add $\frac{7}{12}$ and $\frac{7}{12}$.

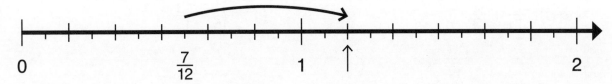

$$\frac{7}{12} + \frac{7}{12} = \boxed{\frac{}{12}} = \boxed{\frac{}{6}} = 1\boxed{\frac{}{6}}$$

3 Subtract $\frac{7}{9}$ from $\frac{13}{9}$. Express the answer in simplest form.

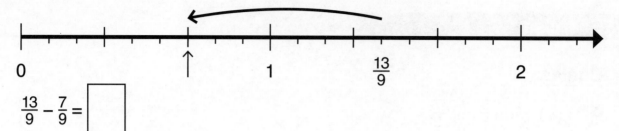

$\frac{13}{9} - \frac{7}{9} = \boxed{}$

Practice

Express answers 1 or greater as whole or mixed numbers. Use simplest form.

4 Add or subtract.

(a) $\frac{1}{12} + \frac{5}{12}$

(b) $\frac{4}{8} + \frac{5}{8}$

(c) $\frac{9}{10} - \frac{5}{10}$

(d) $\frac{7}{10} + \frac{9}{10}$

(e) $\frac{11}{13} - \frac{4}{13}$

(f) $\frac{11}{15} + \frac{13}{15}$

(g) $\frac{15}{8} - \frac{11}{8}$

(h) $\frac{23}{20} + \frac{17}{20}$

(i) $\frac{4}{25} + \frac{9}{25} + \frac{7}{25}$

(j) $\frac{23}{30} - \frac{17}{30}$

5 A bag of rice weighs $\frac{13}{16}$ lb. A bag of wheat berries weighs $\frac{9}{16}$ lb more than the bag of rice. A bag of rye berries weighs $\frac{11}{16}$ lb less than the bag of wheat berries. What is the total weight of all three bags of grain?

Challenge

6 Write the missing digits. The fractions should be less than 1.

(a) $\frac{5}{6} + \boxed{\dfrac{}{6}} = 1\boxed{\dfrac{2}{}}$

(b) $\boxed{\dfrac{}{15}} - \boxed{\dfrac{8}{}} = \boxed{\dfrac{}{3}}$

Basics

1 (a) Add $\frac{3}{4}$ and $\frac{7}{12}$.

$$\frac{3}{4} + \frac{7}{12} = \boxed{\frac{}{12}} + \frac{7}{12}$$

$$= \boxed{\frac{}{12}}$$

$$= 1\boxed{\frac{}{12}}$$

$$= 1\boxed{\frac{}{3}}$$

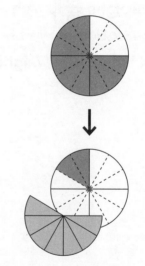

(b) Subtract $\frac{7}{12}$ from $\frac{3}{4}$.

$$\frac{3}{4} - \frac{7}{12} = \boxed{\frac{}{12}} - \frac{7}{12}$$

$$= \boxed{\frac{}{12}}$$

$$= \boxed{\frac{}{6}}$$

2 Add $\frac{2}{3}$ and $\frac{5}{6}$.

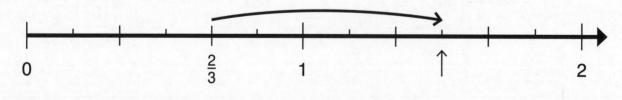

$$\frac{2}{3} + \frac{5}{6} = \boxed{\frac{}{6}} + \frac{5}{6} = \boxed{\frac{}{6}} = \boxed{\frac{}{2}} = 1\boxed{\frac{}{2}}$$

3 Subtract $\frac{11}{15}$ from $\frac{4}{3}$. Express the answer in simplest form.

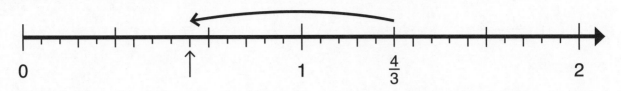

$$\frac{4}{3} - \frac{11}{15} = \boxed{\frac{}{15}} - \frac{11}{15} = \boxed{\frac{}{15}} = \boxed{\frac{}{5}}$$

Practice

Express answers 1 or greater as whole or mixed numbers. Use simplest form.

4 Add.

(a) $\frac{1}{2} + \frac{3}{14}$

(b) $\frac{5}{12} + \frac{3}{4}$

(c) $\frac{9}{8} + \frac{11}{24}$

(d) $\frac{2}{3} + \frac{7}{9}$

(e) $\frac{4}{5} + \frac{3}{10} + \frac{7}{10}$

(f) $\frac{4}{9} + \frac{17}{36} + \frac{11}{18}$

5 Subtract.

(a) $\frac{11}{14} - \frac{4}{7}$

(b) $\frac{5}{6} - \frac{5}{12}$

(c) $\frac{7}{5} - \frac{4}{15}$

(d) $\frac{8}{9} - \frac{2}{3}$

(e) $\frac{24}{25} - \frac{2}{5} - \frac{7}{50}$

(f) $\frac{11}{12} - \frac{2}{3} - \frac{1}{4}$

6 $\frac{3}{10}$ of a pole is painted red, $\frac{1}{5}$ of the pole is painted yellow, and the rest of the pole is painted blue. What fraction of the pole is painted blue?

Basics

1 Add $1\frac{2}{3}$ and $\frac{7}{9}$.

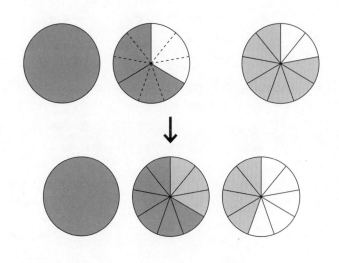

$$1\frac{2}{3} + \frac{7}{9} = 1\frac{\boxed{}}{9} + \frac{7}{9}$$

$$= 1\frac{\boxed{}}{9}$$

$$= 2\frac{\boxed{}}{9}$$

2 Add $1\frac{1}{2}$ and $\frac{5}{6}$.

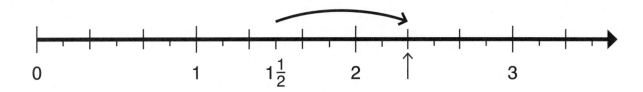

$$1\frac{1}{2} + \frac{5}{6} = 1\frac{\boxed{}}{6} + \frac{5}{6} = 1\frac{\boxed{}}{6} = 1\frac{\boxed{}}{3} = 2\frac{\boxed{}}{3}$$

3 Add $\frac{3}{4}$ and $7\frac{5}{12}$.

$$\frac{3}{4} + 7\frac{5}{12} = \frac{\boxed{}}{12} + 7\frac{5}{12} = 7\frac{\boxed{}}{12} = 7\frac{\boxed{}}{6} = 8\frac{\boxed{}}{6}$$

Practice

Express answers 1 or greater as whole or mixed numbers. Use simplest form.

 Add.

(a) $4\frac{3}{4} + \frac{3}{8}$

(b) $6\frac{1}{2} + \frac{5}{12}$

(c) $\frac{4}{9} + 4\frac{2}{3}$

(d) $8\frac{4}{5} + \frac{7}{20}$

(e) $\frac{11}{14} + 2\frac{4}{7}$

(f) $\frac{5}{6} + 5\frac{13}{18}$

(g) $\frac{1}{6} + \frac{7}{30} + 3\frac{1}{3}$

(h) $\frac{2}{3} + 6\frac{3}{4} + \frac{7}{12}$

5 Aurora ran $3\frac{3}{4}$ miles on Saturday. On Sunday, she ran $\frac{5}{12}$ miles farther than on Saturday. How far did she run altogether?

Challenge

6 Complete each problem using the given digits. Fractions should all be in simplest form.

(a) 12, 13, 14, 15

$$\boxed{\dfrac{}{24}} + \boxed{}\boxed{\dfrac{7}{8}} = \boxed{}\boxed{\dfrac{5}{}}$$

(b) 1, 3, 4, 5, 8

$$\boxed{}\boxed{\dfrac{2}{}} + \boxed{\dfrac{}{15}} = \boxed{}\boxed{\dfrac{}{5}}$$

Basics

1 Add.

(a) $6\frac{1}{4} + 7\frac{7}{12} = 13\frac{1}{4} + \frac{7}{12}$

$= 13\,\boxed{\dfrac{}{12}} + \dfrac{7}{12}$

$= 13\,\boxed{\dfrac{}{12}}$

$= 13\,\boxed{\dfrac{}{6}}$

(b) $4\frac{11}{24} + 2\frac{7}{8} = 6\frac{11}{24} + \frac{7}{8}$

$= 6\frac{11}{24} + \boxed{\dfrac{}{24}}$

$= 6\,\boxed{\dfrac{}{24}}$

$= 7\,\boxed{\dfrac{}{24}}$

$= 7\,\boxed{\dfrac{}{3}}$

Practice

2 Add. Express each answer as a mixed number in simplest form.

(a) $7\frac{2}{9} + 4\frac{1}{3}$

(b) $6\frac{1}{2} + 2\frac{5}{14}$

(c) $4\frac{1}{3} + 3\frac{1}{6}$

(d) $8\frac{3}{4} + 4\frac{3}{20}$

(e) $1\frac{9}{12} + 3\frac{2}{3}$

(f) $5\frac{1}{2} + 4\frac{5}{8}$

(g) $6\frac{5}{6} + 2\frac{1}{18}$

(h) $3\frac{3}{4} + 3\frac{7}{12}$

(i) $4\frac{1}{3} + 2\frac{5}{12} + 3\frac{1}{3}$

(j) $1\frac{1}{2} + 6\frac{3}{4} + 5\frac{7}{8}$

3 After using $2\frac{5}{8}$ yards of fabric to make a dress, Gina still had $7\frac{3}{4}$ yards of fabric left. How many yards of fabric did she have at first?

Basics

1 Subtract $\frac{7}{12}$ from $2\frac{1}{4}$.

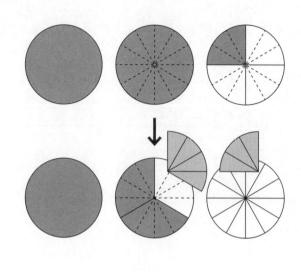

$$2\frac{1}{4} - \frac{7}{12} = 2\boxed{\frac{}{12}} - \frac{7}{12}$$

$$= 1\boxed{\frac{}{12}} - \frac{7}{12}$$

$$= 1\boxed{\frac{}{12}}$$

$$= 1\boxed{\frac{}{3}}$$

2 Subtract $\frac{5}{6}$ from $2\frac{1}{2}$.

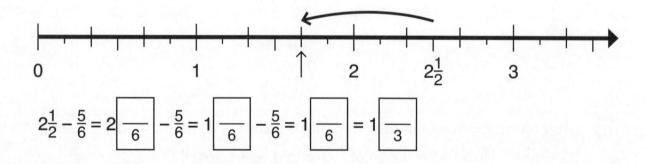

$$2\frac{1}{2} - \frac{5}{6} = 2\boxed{\frac{}{6}} - \frac{5}{6} = 1\boxed{\frac{}{6}} - \frac{5}{6} = 1\boxed{\frac{}{6}} = 1\boxed{\frac{}{3}}$$

3 Subtract $\frac{5}{8}$ from $5\frac{5}{16}$.

$$5\frac{5}{16} - \frac{5}{8} = 5\frac{5}{16} - \boxed{\frac{}{16}} = 4\boxed{\frac{}{16}} - \boxed{\frac{}{16}} = 4\boxed{\frac{}{16}}$$

Practice

Express all answers as mixed numbers in simplest form.

4 Subtract.

(a) $4\frac{3}{4} - \frac{3}{8}$

(b) $4\frac{8}{9} - \frac{2}{3}$

(c) $6\frac{1}{2} - \frac{7}{12}$

(d) $8\frac{4}{5} - \frac{7}{20}$

(e) $9\frac{5}{14} - \frac{4}{7}$

(f) $3\frac{1}{6} - \frac{13}{18}$

(g) $8\frac{1}{6} - \frac{7}{30} - \frac{1}{3}$

(h) $9\frac{2}{3} - \frac{3}{4} - \frac{7}{12}$

5 Andrei spent $3\frac{1}{2}$ hours working in his garden on Saturday. He spent $\frac{3}{4}$ of an hour less time working in his garden on Sunday than on Saturday. How much time did he spend working in his garden on Sunday?

Challenge

6 Complete each problem using the given digits. All numbers should be in simplest form.

(a) 1, 2, 3

$$\boxed{}\,\boxed{\dfrac{1}{6}} - \boxed{\dfrac{2}{}} = \boxed{\dfrac{1}{}}$$

(b) 3, 4, 7, 8, 9, 21

$$\boxed{}\,\boxed{\dfrac{5}{}} - \boxed{\dfrac{2}{}} = \boxed{}\,\boxed{\dfrac{}{}}$$

Basics

1 Subtract.

(a) $7\frac{5}{16} - 2\frac{7}{8} = 5\frac{5}{16} - \frac{7}{8}$

$$= 5\frac{5}{16} - \boxed{\frac{}{16}}$$

$$= 4\boxed{\frac{}{16}} - \boxed{\frac{}{16}}$$

$$= 4\boxed{\frac{}{16}}$$

(b) $6\frac{1}{3} - 3\frac{7}{12} = 3\frac{1}{3} - \frac{7}{12}$

$$= 3\boxed{\frac{}{12}} - \frac{7}{12}$$

$$= 2\boxed{\frac{}{12}} - \frac{7}{12}$$

$$= 2\boxed{\frac{}{12}}$$

$$= 2\boxed{\frac{}{4}}$$

Practice

2 Subtract. Express each answer as a mixed number in simplest form.

(a) $8 - 4\frac{1}{5}$

(b) $12 - 7\frac{5}{16}$

(c) $6\frac{1}{2} - 2\frac{3}{10}$

(d) $7\frac{5}{9} - 4\frac{1}{3}$

(e) $9\frac{1}{6} - 3\frac{1}{3}$ (f) $5\frac{1}{2} - 4\frac{5}{8}$

(g) $8\frac{1}{4} - 3\frac{7}{12}$ (h) $10\frac{5}{12} - 3\frac{2}{3}$

(i) $12 - 2\frac{5}{24} - 3\frac{1}{3}$ (j) $14\frac{1}{2} - 6\frac{3}{4} - 1\frac{7}{8}$

3 Eli had a board that was $9\frac{1}{2}$ m long. He cut off 2 pieces, one $3\frac{3}{10}$ m long and the other $2\frac{4}{5}$ m long. How long is the third piece of the board in meters?

Check

Express answers 1 or greater as whole or mixed numbers. Use simplest form.

1 Find the values.

(a) $\frac{5}{9} + \frac{2}{3}$

(b) $6\frac{9}{12} + \frac{5}{12}$

(c) $10\frac{1}{3} - 7\frac{2}{3}$

(d) $8\frac{4}{5} + 1\frac{7}{15}$

(e) $3\frac{5}{14} - \frac{4}{7}$

(f) $5\frac{13}{18} - 2\frac{5}{6}$

(g) $8\frac{1}{6} + \frac{7}{30} + 3\frac{1}{2}$

(h) $5\frac{27}{28} - 2\frac{3}{7} - \frac{13}{14}$

2 Complete each pattern by following the rule. Use whole or mixed numbers when possible, and simplest form.

(a) Add $\frac{2}{3}$.

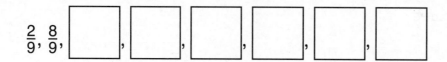

$\frac{2}{9}, \frac{8}{9},$ ☐ , ☐ , ☐ , ☐ , ☐ , ☐

(b) Subtract $\frac{3}{8}$.

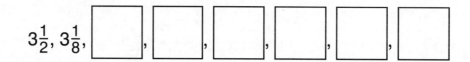

$3\frac{1}{2}, 3\frac{1}{8},$ ☐ , ☐ , ☐ , ☐ , ☐ , ☐

(c) Add $2\frac{5}{12}$.

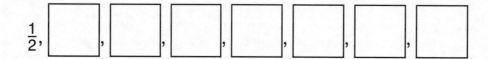

$\frac{1}{2},$ ☐ , ☐ , ☐ , ☐ , ☐ , ☐ , ☐

(d) Subtract $1\frac{3}{4}$.

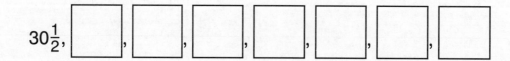

$30\frac{1}{2},$ ☐ , ☐ , ☐ , ☐ , ☐ , ☐ , ☐

3 Evan spent $2\frac{2}{3}$ hours practicing the piano in the morning. He spent another $1\frac{2}{3}$ hours practicing in the afternoon. How many hours did he practice in all?

4 A railroad track-laying machine laid $1\frac{1}{5}$ km of track on Monday and $\frac{17}{20}$ km of track on Tuesday. How many more kilometers of track did it lay on Monday than on Tuesday?

5 Package A weighs $4\frac{1}{2}$ pounds. Package B weighs $2\frac{1}{8}$ pounds more than Package A. What is the total weight of the two packages?

6 Catalina had $6\frac{3}{4}$ cups of flour. She used $2\frac{1}{2}$ cups of flour in one recipe and $2\frac{1}{4}$ cups of flour in another recipe. How much flour does she have left?

Challenge

7 Write + or − in each ◯ to make each equation true.

(a) $\frac{13}{18}$ ◯ $\frac{1}{9}$ ◯ $\frac{1}{2}$ ◯ $\frac{2}{3}$ = 1

(b) $\frac{3}{4}$ ◯ $\frac{13}{24}$ ◯ $\frac{5}{8}$ ◯ $\frac{1}{6}$ = 1

8 This is a way to express 37 using five 3s and the addition symbol: $33 + 3 + \frac{3}{3}$.

(a) Use four 9s to express 100.

(b) Use five 4s to express 55.

(c) Use four 9s to express 20.

(d) Use three each of 1, 3, 5, and 7 to express 20.

Chapter 8 Multiplying a Fraction and a Whole Number

Basics

1 Find the value of 3 groups of $\frac{1}{9}$.

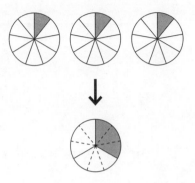

$3 \times \frac{1}{9} = \frac{3 \times 1}{9}$

$= \frac{\boxed{}}{9}$

$= \frac{\boxed{}}{3}$

2 Find the value of 5 groups of $\frac{1}{3}$.

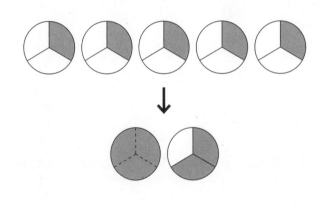

$5 \times \frac{1}{3} = \frac{5 \times 1}{3}$

$= \frac{\boxed{}}{3}$

$= 1\frac{\boxed{}}{3}$

3 How many $\frac{1}{4}$s are in $5\frac{3}{4}$?

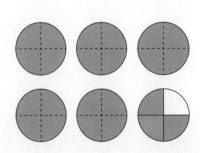

$5\frac{3}{4} = \frac{\boxed{}}{4}$

$= \boxed{} \times \frac{1}{4}$

There are _____ $\frac{1}{4}$s in $5\frac{3}{4}$.

4 Express the products as mixed numbers in simplest form.

(a) Find the product of 16 and $\frac{1}{5}$.

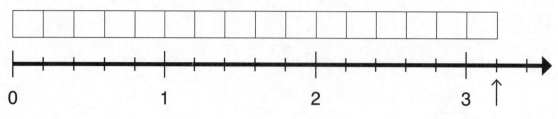

$16 \times \frac{1}{5} =$

(b) Find the product of 16 and $\frac{1}{6}$.

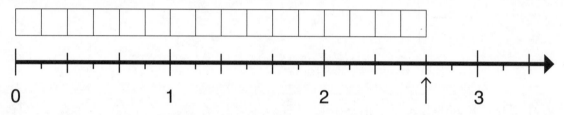

$16 \times \frac{1}{6} =$

Practice

Express answers 1 or greater as whole or mixed numbers. Use simplest form.

5 Multiply.

(a) $5 \times \frac{1}{8}$

(b) $7 \times \frac{1}{12}$

(c) $5 \times \frac{1}{5}$

(d) $8 \times \frac{1}{10}$

(e) $6 \times \frac{1}{3}$

(f) $20 \times \frac{1}{4}$

(g) $8 \times \frac{1}{5}$

(h) $10 \times \frac{1}{8}$

(i) $15 \times \frac{1}{9}$

(j) $30 \times \frac{1}{15}$

6 A jug has 4 L of juice. $\frac{1}{3}$ L of juice was poured into each of 10 glasses. How many liters of juice are still in the jug?

Basics

1 Find the value of 3 groups of $\frac{3}{4}$.

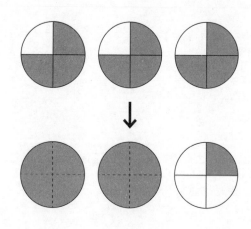

$3 \times \frac{3}{4} = \frac{3 \times 3}{4}$

$= \boxed{\dfrac{}{4}}$

$= 2\boxed{\dfrac{}{4}}$

2 Find the product of 5 and $\frac{2}{3}$.

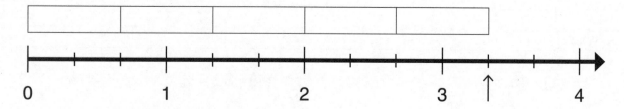

$5 \times \frac{2}{3} = \frac{5 \times 2}{3} = \boxed{\dfrac{}{}} = \boxed{}\boxed{\dfrac{}{}}$

3 Find the product of 7 and $\frac{2}{9}$. Express the answer as a mixed number.

$7 \times \frac{2}{9}$

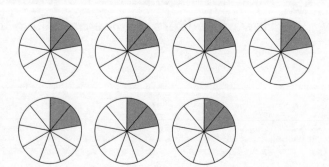

Practice

Express answers 1 or greater as whole or mixed numbers. Use simplest form.

4 Multiply.

(a) $2 \times \frac{3}{7}$

(b) $7 \times \frac{5}{12}$

(c) $3 \times \frac{3}{5}$

(d) $9 \times \frac{3}{10}$

(e) $5 \times \frac{5}{6}$

(f) $5 \times \frac{3}{7}$

(g) $7 \times \frac{5}{11}$

(h) $8 \times \frac{7}{15}$

5 A park $1\frac{3}{5}$ miles from Carter's home has a trail around it that is $\frac{9}{10}$ mile long. Carter ran to the park, ran the trail 3 times, and then ran home. How far did he run in all?

Basics

1 Find the value of 4 groups of $\frac{3}{4}$.

(a) $4 \times \frac{3}{4} = \frac{4 \times 3}{4}$

$= \dfrac{}{4}$

$= \boxed{}$

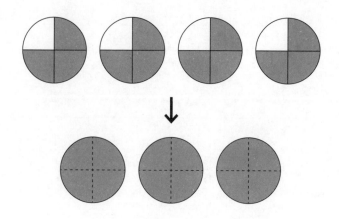

(b) $4 \times \frac{3}{4} = \dfrac{\overset{1}{\cancel{4}} \times 3}{\underset{1}{\cancel{4}}} = \boxed{}$

2 Find the value of 4 groups of $\frac{7}{10}$.

$4 \times \frac{7}{10} = \dfrac{\overset{2}{\cancel{4}} \times 7}{\underset{5}{\cancel{10}}}$

$= \dfrac{}{5}$

$= \boxed{}\,\boxed{\dfrac{}{}}$

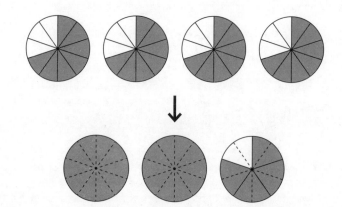

3 Find the product of 6 and $\frac{5}{9}$.

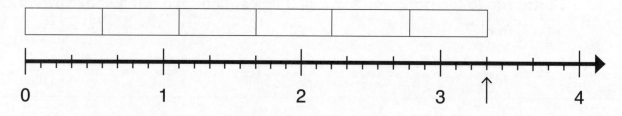

$6 \times \frac{5}{9} = \dfrac{6 \times 5}{9} = \dfrac{}{3} = \boxed{}\,\boxed{\dfrac{}{}}$

Practice

Express answers 1 or greater as whole or mixed numbers. Use simplest form.

4 Multiply.

(a) $3 \times \frac{2}{9}$

(b) $8 \times \frac{3}{4}$

(c) $15 \times \frac{2}{5}$

(d) $3 \times \frac{5}{6}$

(e) $8 \times \frac{3}{10}$

(f) $10 \times \frac{3}{8}$

(g) $15 \times \frac{4}{9}$

(h) $15 \times \frac{5}{12}$

5 One wall of Allysa's room is 3 m long. She is making a ceiling border for that wall by pasting $\frac{3}{10}$ m pieces of wallpaper trim end-to-end. So far she has pasted 9 pieces of trim. How long does she have to make the last piece of trim to complete the project?

Challenge

6 Use the given digits so each expression has the greatest possible value. Express the answer as a mixed number in simplest form.

(a) 4, 5, 6 $\boxed{} \times \dfrac{\boxed{}}{\boxed{}} =$

(b) 6, 7, 8, 9 $\boxed{} \times \dfrac{\boxed{}}{\boxed{}} + \boxed{} =$

7 Use the given digits so each expression has the least possible value. Express the answer as a mixed number in simplest form.

(a) 4, 5, 6 $\boxed{} \times \dfrac{\boxed{}}{\boxed{}} =$

(b) 6, 7, 8, 9 $\boxed{} \times \dfrac{\boxed{}}{\boxed{}} + \boxed{} =$

Basics

1

_____ out of 5 children are boys.

$\dfrac{}{5}$ of the children are boys.

_____ out of 5 children are girls.

$\dfrac{}{5}$ of the children are girls.

2

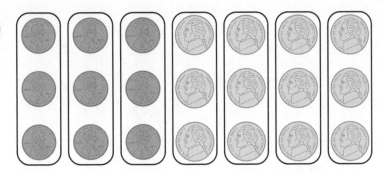

(a) _____ out of 21 coins are pennies.

$\dfrac{}{21}$ of the coins are pennies.

_____ out of 7 groups of coins are pennies.

$\dfrac{}{7}$ of the coins are pennies.

(b) What fraction of the coins are nickels? Express the answer in simplest form.

Practice

Express all answers in simplest form.

3 What fraction of each set of stars is shaded?

(a)

(b)

(c)

(d)

(e)

(f)

(g)

(h)

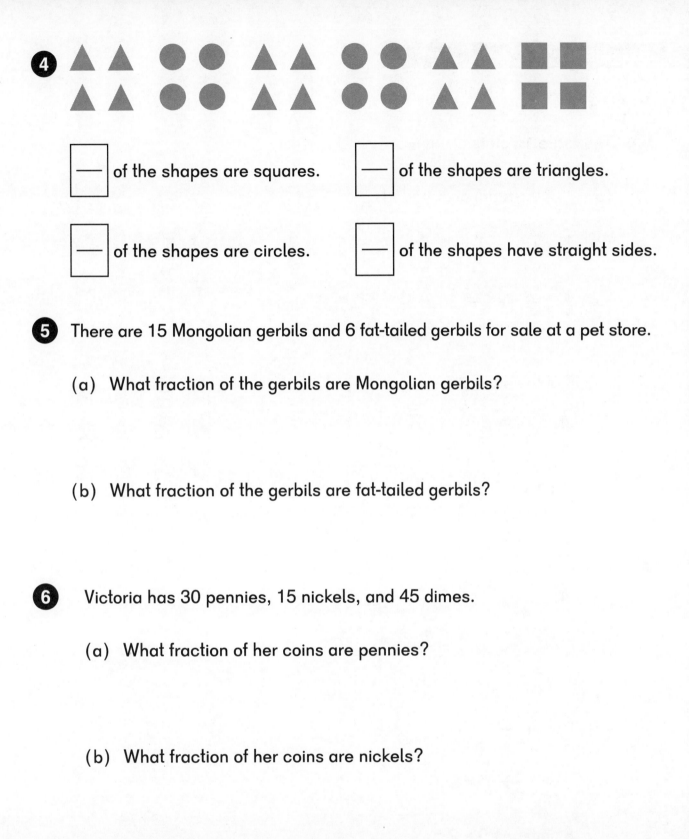

4

$\boxed{}$ of the shapes are squares.

$\boxed{}$ of the shapes are triangles.

$\boxed{}$ of the shapes are circles.

$\boxed{}$ of the shapes have straight sides.

5 There are 15 Mongolian gerbils and 6 fat-tailed gerbils for sale at a pet store.

(a) What fraction of the gerbils are Mongolian gerbils?

(b) What fraction of the gerbils are fat-tailed gerbils?

6 Victoria has 30 pennies, 15 nickels, and 45 dimes.

(a) What fraction of her coins are pennies?

(b) What fraction of her coins are nickels?

(c) What fraction of her coins are dimes?

Basics

1 There are 15 stars.

(a) $\frac{1}{5}$ of the stars are shaded.

$\frac{1}{5}$ of 15 $\longrightarrow$ $\frac{15}{5}$ = ☐

$\frac{1}{5} \times 15 = \frac{1 \times \overset{3}{\cancel{15}}}{\underset{1}{\cancel{5}}}$ = ☐

(b) $\frac{4}{5}$ of the stars are shaded.

$\frac{4}{5}$ of 15 $\longrightarrow$ 4 × $\frac{15}{5}$ = ☐

$\frac{4}{5} \times 15 = \frac{4 \times \overset{3}{\cancel{15}}}{\underset{1}{\cancel{5}}}$ = ☐

2 Find $\frac{5}{8}$ of 16.

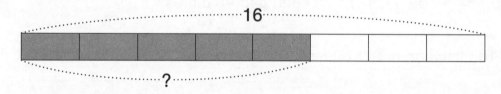

(a) 8 units $\longrightarrow$ 16

1 unit $\longrightarrow$ $\frac{16}{8}$ = 2

5 units $\longrightarrow$ 5 × 2 = ☐

(b) $\frac{5}{8} \times 16 = \frac{5 \times \overset{2}{\cancel{16}}}{\underset{1}{\cancel{8}}}$ = ☐

Practice

Express all answers in simplest form.

3 (a) $\frac{1}{2}$ of 8 $\longrightarrow$ $\frac{1}{2} \times 8 =$

(b) $\frac{1}{3}$ of 6 $\longrightarrow$ $\frac{1}{3} \times 6 =$

$\frac{2}{3}$ of 6 $\longrightarrow$ $\frac{2}{3} \times 6 =$

(c) $\frac{1}{6}$ of 12 $\longrightarrow$ $\frac{1}{6} \times 12 =$

$\frac{5}{6}$ of 12 $\longrightarrow$ $\frac{5}{6} \times 12 =$

(d) $\frac{1}{7} \times 21 =$

$\frac{3}{7} \times 21 =$

$\frac{5}{7} \times 21 =$

(e) $\frac{1}{2} \times 30 =$

$\frac{3}{5} \times 30 =$

$\frac{5}{6} \times 30 =$

$\frac{7}{10} \times 30 =$

4 Find the value of each of the following.

(a) $\frac{1}{2} \times 16$

(b) $\frac{3}{4} \times 12$

(c) $\frac{2}{5} \times 100$

(d) $\frac{1}{9} \times 180$

(e) $\frac{2}{3} \times 60$

(f) $\frac{3}{8} \times 56$

(g) $\frac{2}{3} \times 48$

(h) $\frac{7}{10} \times 120$

5 A dog has 42 teeth. $\frac{2}{7}$ of a dog's teeth are incisors, which are used for tearing meat from bones and for self-grooming. How many incisors does a dog have?

Basics

1 (a) Find $\frac{1}{3}$ of 8.

$$\frac{1}{3} \times 8 = \frac{8}{3}$$

$$= \boxed{}\ \boxed{\dfrac{}{}}$$

(b) Find $\frac{2}{3}$ of 8.

$$\frac{2}{3} \times 8 = \frac{2 \times 8}{3}$$

$$= \boxed{\dfrac{}{3}}$$

$$= \boxed{}\ \boxed{\dfrac{}{}}$$

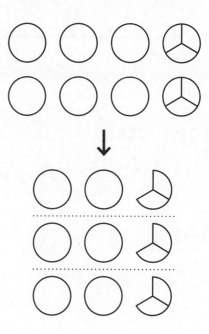

2 (a) Find $\frac{1}{6}$ of 9.

$$\frac{1}{6} \times 9 = \frac{\overset{3}{\cancel{9}}}{\underset{2}{\cancel{6}}}$$

$$= \boxed{}\ \boxed{\dfrac{}{}}$$

(b) Find $\frac{5}{6}$ of 9.

$$\frac{5}{6} \times 9 = \frac{5 \times \overset{3}{\cancel{9}}}{\underset{2}{\cancel{6}}}$$

$$= \boxed{\dfrac{}{2}}$$

$$= \boxed{}\ \boxed{\dfrac{}{}}$$

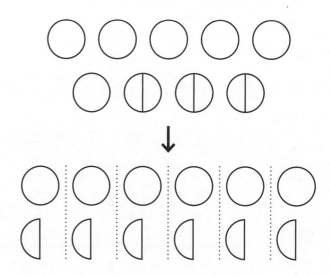

3 Find $\frac{5}{9}$ of 6.

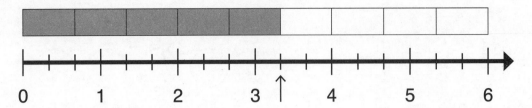

$$\frac{5}{9} \times 6 = \frac{5 \times \overset{2}{\cancel{6}}}{\underset{3}{\cancel{9}}} = \boxed{} = \boxed{}\boxed{}$$

Practice

Express answers 1 or greater as whole or mixed numbers. Use simplest form.

4 Find the value of each of the following.

(a)

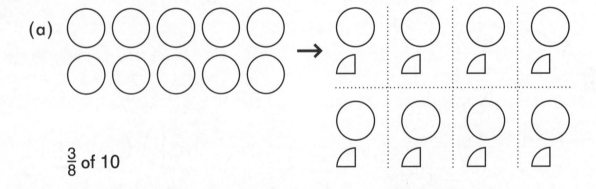

$\frac{3}{8}$ of 10

(b)

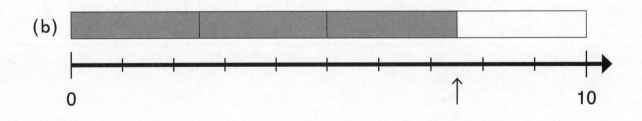

$\frac{3}{4}$ of 10

5 Find the value of each of the following.

(a) $\frac{1}{2}$ of 9

(b) $\frac{1}{3}$ of 10

(c) $\frac{2}{9} \times 4$

(d) $\frac{5}{9} \times 3$

(e) $\frac{3}{4} \times 30$

(f) $\frac{7}{8} \times 20$

(g) $\frac{3}{7} \times 18$

(h) $\frac{7}{10} \times 15$

6 Does $\frac{5}{8}$ of a 12 lb bag of beans weigh more or less than twelve $\frac{5}{8}$ lb bags of beans?

Basics

1 A cat has 30 teeth. If $\frac{2}{5}$ of a cat's teeth are incisors, how many teeth are not incisors?

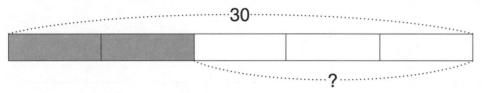

5 units ⟶ 30

1 unit ⟶ $\frac{30}{5}$ =

3 units ⟶

2 $\frac{2}{5}$ of Asimah's books are nonfiction. The rest are fiction. If she has 30 nonfiction books, how many books does she have?

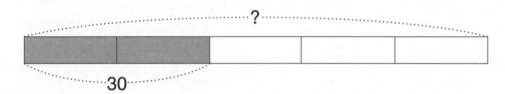

3 A water tank is $\frac{2}{5}$ full. It takes another 30 gallons to fill it up. How many gallons of water does the tank hold?

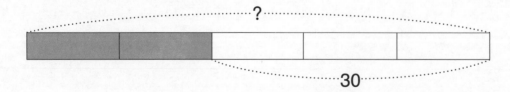

Practice

4 There are 56 members in a paddling club. $\frac{5}{7}$ of them are adults and the rest are children. How many children are in the club?

5 There are 135 helium balloons at a party. $\frac{2}{9}$ of them are blue. There are as many red balloons as blue balloons. The rest of the balloons are yellow. How many balloons are yellow?

6 Gary traveled by train for 400 miles of his trip. He took a bus for the remaining $\frac{3}{8}$ of the trip. How many miles was his trip?

7 Lee made a brick mailbox using two colors of bricks. $\frac{5}{12}$ of the bricks were light red and the rest were dark red. If he used 85 light red bricks, how many bricks did he use in all?

Challenge

8 After $\frac{3}{5}$ of a bag of flour was used to make bread, there were 9 kg of flour left. How many kilograms of flour were in the bag at first?

9 If $\frac{7}{15}$ of a number is 35, what is $\frac{3}{5}$ of the number?

Basics

1 Anna spent 21 days on a vacation. 14 of them were spent at the beach and the remaining days were spent hiking in the mountains. What fraction of her vacation was spent in the mountains?

21 − 14 = ☐

_____ out of 21 days were spent in the mountains.

$\dfrac{\boxed{}}{21} = \dfrac{\boxed{}}{3}$

_____ of her vacation was spent in the mountains.

2 On the way home from the park, Jody ran for $\frac{3}{5}$ of the way, jogged for $\frac{1}{10}$ of the way, and walked the remaining 360 m. How far was the park from her home in meters?

$\dfrac{3}{5} = \dfrac{6}{10}$

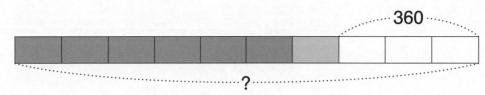

3 Fadiya had 92 tropical fish. She gave 8 of them to her friend, and then sold $\frac{2}{7}$ of the remaining fish. How many fish does she have now?

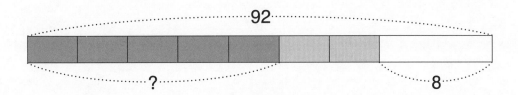

Practice

4 Jack is driving from town to his farm 36 miles away. 25 miles of the road are paved, 7 miles are gravel, and the remaining miles are dirt. What fraction of the trip is on a dirt road?

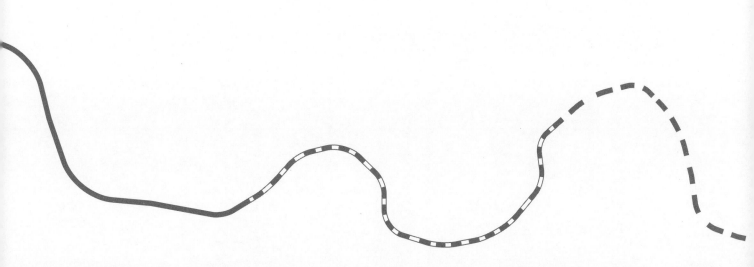

5 Aurora baked some cookies. She gave 12 cookies to her family, and then sold $\frac{7}{9}$ of the cookies at a bake sale. She had 8 cookies left over. How many cookies did she bake?

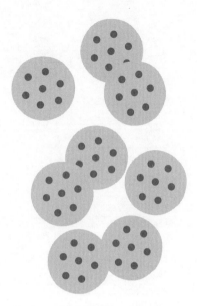

6 On a math team, 6 students are from the third grade, 9 students are from the fourth grade, and $\frac{4}{9}$ of the students are from the fifth grade. How many students are from the fifth grade?

7 Land area is measured in acres. On a farm, $\frac{1}{12}$ of the land is used to grow clover, $\frac{1}{4}$ is used to grow wheat, $\frac{1}{3}$ is used to grow rye, and the remaining 8 acres is used to grow oats. How many acres is the land that is being planted?

Challenge

8 There are twelve flags spaced equally along a track. Runners start at the first flag. A runner reaches the 8th flag in 8 seconds. If he runs the whole time at the same speed, in how many seconds will he reach the 11th flag?

Check

Express answers 1 or greater as whole or mixed numbers. Use simplest form.

1 Multiply.

(a) $15 \times \frac{1}{5}$

(b) $12 \times \frac{2}{3}$

(c) $6 \times \frac{5}{9}$

(d) $4 \times \frac{7}{30}$

(e) $\frac{3}{5} \times 10$

(f) $\frac{7}{8} \times 40$

(g) $\frac{3}{7} \times 8$

(h) $\frac{13}{20} \times 480$

2 (a) $24 \times \boxed{\dfrac{}{}} = 8$ (b) $36 \times \boxed{\dfrac{}{}} = 9$

3 A nail is $\frac{5}{8}$ inches long. How many inches are 7 nails placed end-to-end?

4 Because of the lower gravity of the moon, a person weighs about $\frac{4}{25}$ as much on the moon as on Earth. About how much would a 75 pound person weigh on the moon?

5 Because of the lower gravity of Mars, a person who weighs 200 pounds on Earth would weigh 76 pounds on Mars.

(a) A weight on Mars is what fraction of a weight on Earth?

(b) How much would a 75 pound person weigh on Mars?

6 There are some balloons at a party. $\frac{2}{9}$ of the balloons are black, $\frac{1}{3}$ of them are orange, and the remaining 16 balloons are yellow. How many balloons are there?

7 On a farm, there are 60 sheep. 16 are Leicester sheep. There are twice as many Merino sheep as Leicester sheep. The rest are Dorset sheep. What fraction of the sheep are Dorset sheep?

8 Amelia has 24 toy cars. She gave $\frac{3}{4}$ of her cars to Carter. Carter gave $\frac{2}{3}$ of the cars he got from Amelia to Eli. Eli gave $\frac{1}{2}$ of the cars he got from Carter to Grace. How many cars did Grace get from Eli?

9 A chess club has a tournament once a month. Last month, $\frac{3}{4}$ of the members attended the tournament. This month, $\frac{3}{8}$ of the members did not attend the tournament. If there were 24 members that did not attend the tournament this month, how many members were at the tournament last month?

Challenge

10 8 stakes are spaced evenly apart in a garden. If the distance between two of them is $\frac{4}{7}$ m, how many meters is the distance from the first stake to the last stake?

11 $\frac{1}{5}$ of $\frac{1}{3}$ of $\frac{1}{2}$ of a number is 25. What is the number?

12 Jordan ate $\frac{3}{4}$ of the rice crackers in a package plus another 3 crackers. Adam then ate $\frac{3}{4}$ of the remaining crackers and another 3 crackers. If there were 3 crackers left, how many crackers were in the package at first?

Chapter 9 Line Graphs and Line Plots

Basics

1 This table shows the number of days it snowed each month from October to June at Cloud Ski Resort. A graph of the same data is partially completed.

Month	Oct	Nov	Dec	Jan	Feb	Mar	Apr	May	Jun
Number of Days of Snow	0	7	8	26	16	20	7	3	1

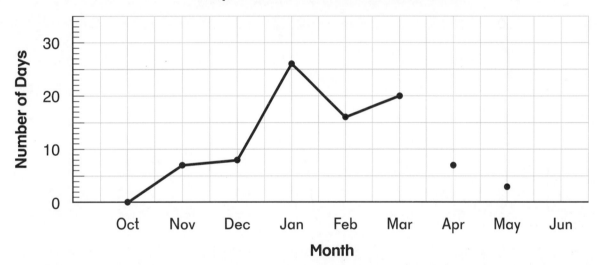

Days of Snowfall at Cloud Ski Resort

(a) Complete the graph.

(b) Which three months had the most days of snowfall?

(c) The greatest change in the number of days of snowfall was between which two months? Was this change an increase or a decrease?

Practice

2 This table shows the greatest snow depth, in inches, each month from October to June at a ski resort. A graph of the same data is partially completed.

Month	Oct	Nov	Dec	Jan	Feb	Mar	Apr	May	Jun
Depth (in)	0	20	63	155	180	168	160	155	80

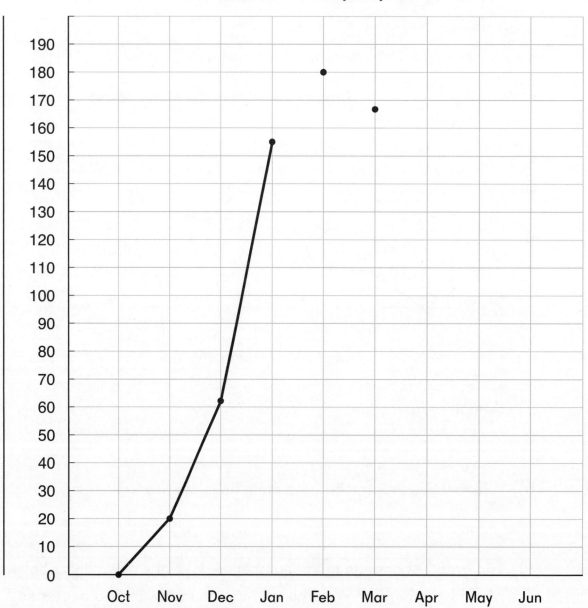

Greatest Snow Depth by Month

9-1 Line Graphs

(a) Plot the rest of the points and connect them with lines.

(b) What does the vertical axis represent? Label it.

(c) What does the horizontal axis represent? Label it.

(d) How many inches does each increment between tick marks represent?

(e) In which month was the snow the deepest?

(f) Between which two months was the sharpest increase in snow depth?

(g) By how many inches did the snow depth fall between January and June?

(h) Which months might be the best time to plan a ski trip when there is fresh snow?

3 This table shows the number of people that visited a museum each day for one week.

Day	Mon	Tues	Wed	Thur	Fri	Sat	Sun
Number of People	35	25	12	20	42	60	55

Which three of the following graphs could be accurate representations of the data?

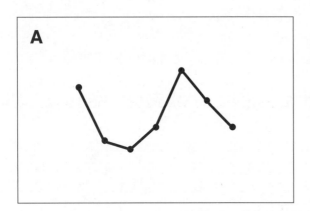

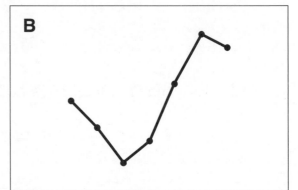

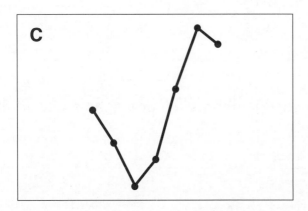

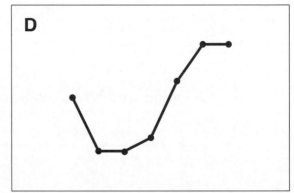

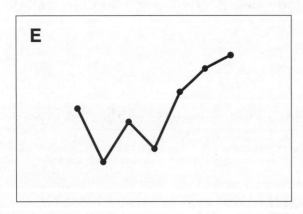

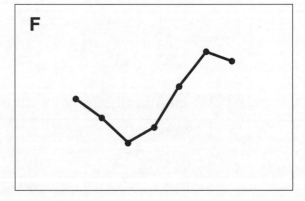

Basics

1 The following table shows the number of children each week at the 8 sessions of a karate class.

Session	1	2	3	4	5	6	7	8
Number of Children	30	25	20	23	17	15	12	20

Complete the graph below to show this information.

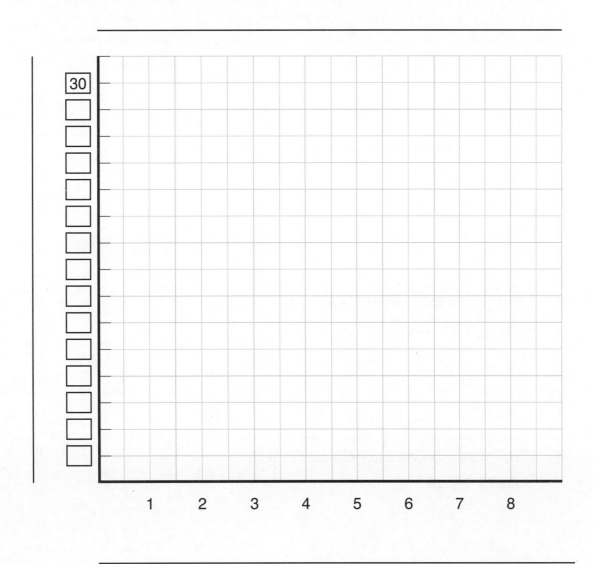

Practice

2 Misha recorded the weight of her Shih Tzu puppy, Sofie, every 2 weeks for the first 36 weeks. The data is shown in the table below.

(a) Complete the line graph on the next page. Include a title, label the axes, and label the increments.

(b) At about how many weeks did Sofie's growth rate start slowing down?

(c) At about how many weeks old was Sofie full grown?

(d) From the graph, estimate Sofie's weight at 17 weeks.

(e) What would be an expected weight for Sofie at 1 year?

Weeks	Weight (Ounces)
Birth	6
2	16
4	24
6	29
8	39
10	45
12	53
14	60
16	70
18	74
20	81
22	86
24	93
26	95
28	96
30	98
32	99
34	98
36	98

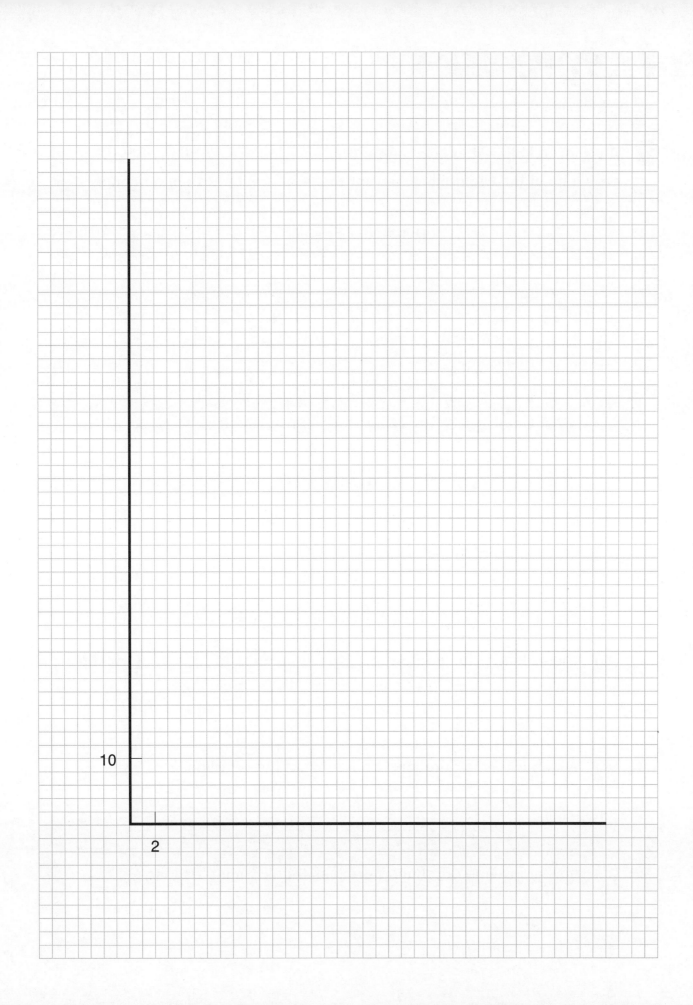

Basics

1 A visitor at Yellowstone National Park recorded the duration of the eruptions of the Old Faithful Geyser to the nearest fourth of a minute.

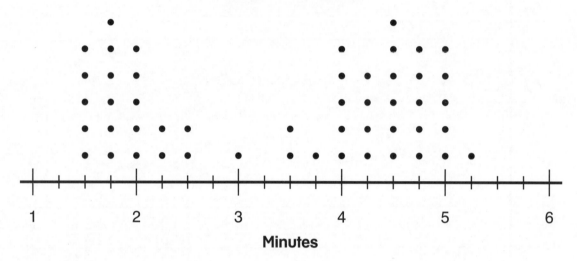

Duration of Eruptions

Minutes

(a) How many eruptions did he record?

(b) The eruptions lasted from _____ minutes to _____ minutes.

(c) Which two time durations were most of the eruptions?

(d) How many time durations were less than $3\frac{1}{4}$ minutes long?

Practice

2 Jaiden asked some students how long it took them to get to school, rounded to the nearest 5 minutes, and listed their answers.

10	20	5	25	15	10	30	15	25	20	25	40	30	15	35
20	25	35	15	30	20	40	10	30	15	10	50	45	20	25

(a) Use this data to complete the line plot below.

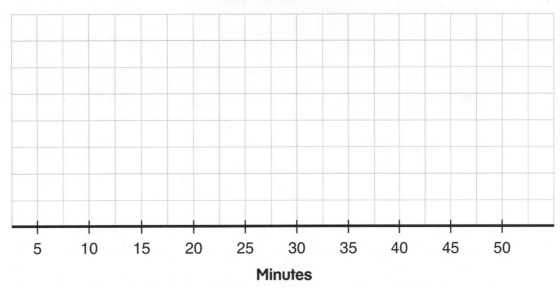

Travel Time to School

Minutes

(b) What are the most common travel times?

(c) What is the difference between the longest and shortest travel times?

(d) How many students took less than half an hour to travel to school?

(e) What fraction of the students took more than half an hour to travel to school?

3 The students in a fourth grade class were asked to write down the number of hours they slept to the nearest fourth of an hour.

9	$8\frac{3}{4}$	6	$9\frac{1}{4}$	$8\frac{3}{4}$	8	$7\frac{1}{4}$	$9\frac{1}{4}$
$9\frac{1}{2}$	10	$9\frac{1}{2}$	$6\frac{1}{2}$	$9\frac{1}{2}$	9	$9\frac{1}{4}$	$10\frac{1}{4}$
9	$7\frac{1}{4}$	8	$8\frac{1}{2}$	9	$7\frac{3}{4}$	9	11
10	$9\frac{1}{4}$	$8\frac{1}{2}$	$8\frac{3}{4}$	$10\frac{1}{4}$	$9\frac{3}{4}$	$9\frac{1}{2}$	$10\frac{3}{4}$

(a) Complete the line plot below.

Hours of Sleep for Fourth Graders

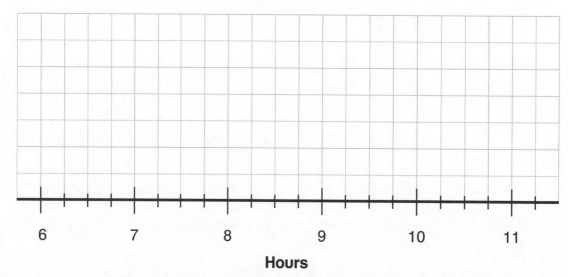

Hours

(b) How many students are included in the data set?

(c) It is recommended that children between 6 and 13 years old get at least 9 hours of sleep. How many students did not get at least 9 hours of sleep?

(d) What fraction of the students got at least 9 hours of sleep?

Check

1 A teacher recorded the number of words some students could type before and after a keyboarding class. These two line plots show the two data sets.

Before the Course

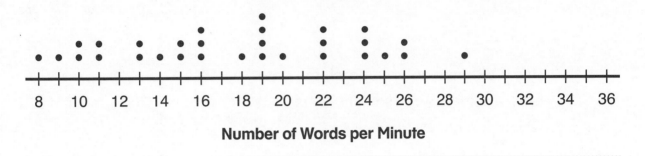

Number of Words per Minute

After the Course

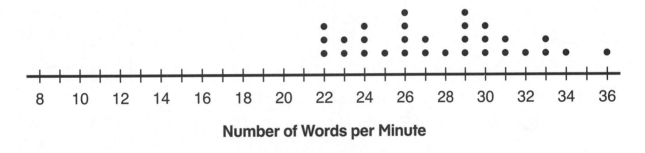

Number of Words per Minute

(a) How many students were in the class?

(b) What was the difference between the least and the greatest number of words students could type in one minute at the beginning of the course?

(c) What was the difference between the least and the greatest number of words students could type in one minute at the end of the course?

(d) Based on the data, was the class helpful? Explain.

2 Jacob's and Sara's heights to the nearest inch was recorded on their birthdays every year from ages 2 to 20. The data is shown in the table below. On the next page, Jacob's data has been graphed. The vertical axis below 30 has been shortened since there are no data values for height less than 30.

(a) Write a title and label the axes on the graph.

(b) Use a different color to graph the data for Sara. Indicate which line is for which person.

(c) From the graph, estimate Jacob's height when he was $3\frac{1}{2}$ years old.

(d) From the graph, estimate Sara's height when she was $11\frac{1}{2}$ years old.

(e) At about what age did Sara stop growing as quickly?

(f) At about what age did Jacob stop growing as quickly?

(g) What other observations can you make from the data?

Age (years)	Height (in) Jacob	Height (in) Sara
2	35	31
3	37	33
4	40	36
5	41	39
6	45	44
7	46	47
8	49	51
9	50	53
10	53	56
11	55	57
12	57	62
13	60	63
14	62	64
15	65	64
16	66	64
17	69	64
18	70	65
19	71	65
20	71	65

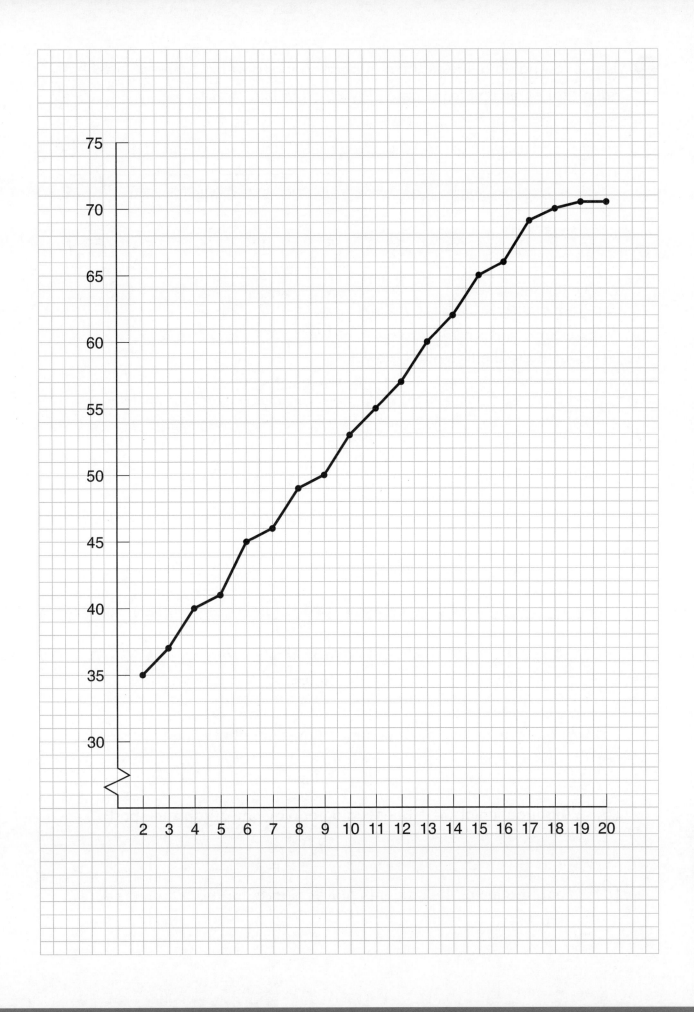

3 The following data shows the number of hours a week, to the nearest half hour, that some children spent playing organized sports.

$2\frac{1}{2}$	0	$1\frac{1}{2}$	5	0	2	$5\frac{1}{2}$	3	0
$9\frac{1}{2}$	$2\frac{1}{2}$	$8\frac{1}{2}$	$2\frac{1}{2}$	$3\frac{1}{2}$	8	5	$1\frac{1}{2}$	$5\frac{1}{2}$
$8\frac{1}{2}$	0	5	$3\frac{1}{2}$	8	3	6	4	3
3	$6\frac{1}{2}$	$2\frac{1}{2}$	9	5	$5\frac{1}{2}$	$2\frac{1}{2}$	$7\frac{1}{2}$	5

(a) Complete the line plot below.

Hours Playing Sports

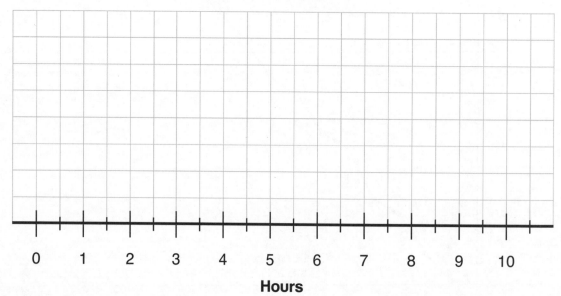

Hours

(b) What were the two most common times spent playing sports?

(c) What fraction of the students did not play any organized sports?

(d) What fraction of the students played sports for more than 5 hours?

Check

1 Write the numbers in order from least to greatest.

(a) $\dfrac{7}{9}, \dfrac{13}{18}, \dfrac{3}{7}, \dfrac{15}{13}, \dfrac{8}{21}$

(b) $\dfrac{43}{7}, \dfrac{31}{5}, \dfrac{63}{8}, \dfrac{49}{9}$

2 Find the values. Express each answer in simplest form.

(a) $3\dfrac{7}{12} - \dfrac{2}{3}$

(b) $\dfrac{5}{8} + \dfrac{3}{4} + \dfrac{1}{2}$

(c) $4\dfrac{1}{2} + 16\dfrac{5}{6}$

(d) $7\dfrac{1}{9} - 5\dfrac{2}{3}$

(e) $12 \times \dfrac{5}{9}$

(f) $\dfrac{7}{8} \times 10$

(g) $\dfrac{2}{7}$ of 98

(h) $39 \div 6$

3 Find three common multiples of 2, 3, and 4 greater than 60 but less than 100.

4 Estimate and then find the quotient and remainder when the difference between 35,004 and 28,683 is divided by 6.

5 Estimate and then find the product when the sum of 4,789 and 589 is multiplied by 35.

6 Victoria has 30 pennies, 15 nickels, and 45 dimes.

(a) What fraction of her coins have a value of more than 1 cent?

(b) If she is given 10 quarters, what fraction of her coins will have a value less than 10 cents?

7 A jewelry store had 60 necklaces. They sold $\frac{3}{5}$ of them for $459 each and the rest for $295 each. How much did they receive from the sales?

8 For an art project, Amy cut a 30 ft piece of yarn into different sized pieces. 10 pieces were $\frac{7}{12}$ ft long and 18 pieces were $\frac{3}{4}$ ft long. How long is the leftover piece of yarn in feet?

9 Mr. Ikeda bought 5 identical lamps, 4 identical chairs, and 2 identical side tables. Each lamp cost half as much as each chair. Each side table cost the same as a lamp and chair combined. If he spent $248 on the chairs, how much did he spend in all?

10 Avery had some blue and white beads. She used half of each type of bead. Then she had 3 times as many blue beads as white beads. How many times as many blue beads as white beads did she have at first?

Challenge

11 Aaron rolls a die. Every time he rolls a prime number, he gets 5 points. Every time he does not roll a prime number, he loses 3 points. At the end of the game, his score is 0. What is the least number of rolls he could have made? (Hint: The points he won and lost must be the same.)

12 There are 12 cards numbered 1–12. Alex, Dion, Mei, Emma, and Sofia each pick 2 cards and find the sum of the two cards they picked.

| 1 | 2 | 3 | 4 | 5 | 6 |

| 7 | 8 | 9 | 10 | 11 | 12 |

Alex	Dion	Mei	Emma	Sofia
16	4	19	11	7

Which 2 cards did each friend pick?